SPUR PUBLICATIONS

POULTRY FANCIERS LIBRARY

General Editors
Dr. J. Batty   Mrs. M. Batty

POULTRY HOUSE
AND APPLIANCES

A Do It Yourself Guide

Poultry Houses and Appliances

A D.I.Y. GUIDE

PUBLISHED BY THE SPUR PUBLICATIONS COMPANY
Hill Brow, Liss, Hampshire, GU33 7PU

THIS EDITION BY
THE SPUR PUBLICATIONS COMPANY, JULY 1976
REPRINTED NOVEMBER, 1976

Previously published by Cassell & Co. Ltd
© Cassell & Co. Ltd, 1976

ISBN 0 904558 16 9

Printed and bound in Great Britain by
Redwood Burn Limited, Trowbridge & Esher
for the publishers
THE SPUR PUBLICATIONS COMPANY
Hill Brow, Liss, Hampshire, GU33 7PU

CONTENTS

v

FOREWORD

Many poultry keepers find themselves having to "knock together" suitable poultry houses. Yet without proper guidance they finish up with unsuitable accommodation, which is often an eyesore and more expensive than it need have been.

The purpose of this DIY GUIDE is to show the domestic poultry keeper or smallholder how he can produce suitable sheds, runs and appliances at reasonable cost. All the requirements are explained, and drawings are given to enable the reader to see what he can achieve by following the instructions.

Many *new materials* are available for improving housing and readers are advised to consider how best these can be utilised. In particular, fibre-glass wool or polystyrene may be employed for insulating sheds and brooders.

For brooders, alternative methods of heating may be considered. Calor gas brooder lamps are available which may be used instead of oil lamps. Alternatively, where electricity is available near the outside brooders, infra red lamps can be employed. These are efficient and economical, especially when the brooders are insulated.

For many reasons this is an age of *Do It Yourself.* With study and application the DIY enthusiast should find this book will more than pay for itself in cost savings.

CHAPTER I

The Building of Poultry Houses

THE SITE.—For a poultry house, the site should be sunny, facing as nearly south as practicable, not too near a dwelling house, but at the same time in a position quite convenient for access in inclement weather. A dry spot should be selected, certainly not one at the bottom of a slope if it can be avoided.

If trouble from damp is anticipated, and the site cannot be changed, the ground should be well banked up with ashes, gravel, or similar material not likely to retain moisture.

In all cases care should be taken that rainwater from the roof is at least thrown well away from the base of the structure. Failing this, harm will soon be caused, and the ground reduced to a soft and dirty condition. It will be all the better if the water can be collected in gutters leading to rainwater butts, or taken in small pipes underground to small " soak-aways "— that is, pits a few yards away, filled with stones or broken bricks, and covered at the top with earth.

In choosing garden position it is often advantageous—other things being equal—to erect a poultry house against an existing fence or wall. This course renders the construction simpler, and also saves the cost of one side of the building. At the same time it should be ascertained that the builder has a right to make use of such a wall or fence, which in some cases may belong entirely to an adjoining owner, whose neighbours will then be well advised not to fix their work to, or in any way interfere with, such erections. It should also be remembered that some neighbours hardly appreciate the proximity of fowls. It is always well to consider neighbours as far as possible, making every effort to spare them any reasonable cause for complaint, thus steering clear of possible annoyance at a later date.

All risk of birds straying on to other people's ground should be guarded against, and the buildings should never be placed in such positions as either to deliver rainwater on to or obstruct any serious amount of sunshine from land in other ownership or occupation; and they should not be unsightly.

Choice of Type of House.—If the house has to adjoin a boundary, the roof can be a " lean-to." A narrow gangway is, however, very desirable, and will be useful for repairs, which can then be done without crossing the boundary. When a gangway has been left the slope might be downwards towards the back, thus intruding less on the adjoining premises and obstructing less sun.

Earth Floors, etc.—The question of flooring is often settled by merely using the natural surface well trodden down; but this must not be damp. Many normally employ gravel or ashes bound together with a little cement and sand, or the following method can be recommended: Begin by levelling the ground roughly. Lay some ashes 2 in. deep or more, and see that they are down tight. Make a dry mixture of sifted ashes or sand and cement, 2 parts of sand to 1 part of cement. When well mixed, add water to make into a plaster, and trowel a layer, say ½ in. thick, all over the floor. It can be made smooth by using a wet trowel, or brushing over gently with a wet brush, and will dry almost as hard as a rock. The floor can be made to slope to the front, if desired, for washing purposes.

Another reliable method is to level the earth floor, cover with a good layer of ashes, make it smooth, and then lay old bricks down evenly without mortar. Damp sand, or fine sifted ashes, with a little cement added, brushed into the cracks and corners, completes the work. Such a floor, after nine years' hard wear and tear, was found to be still splendid and solid. Easy to clean, it is vermin-proof.

Boarded Floors.—These are popularly employed, being ideal where it is necessary to keep the floors well above the ground to avoid damp or the depredations of rats, etc. They must be raised on bearers or " plates " of wood, and kept from contact with the soil. Tongued boarding is the best for the purpose, and can be made up in several units held together with ledges on the under-side. In normal times, the boards may be rendered waterproof by painting with the following mixture, which may also be used for other portions of the work: Heat 1 qt. of tar and stir in ¾ lbs. of finely slaked quicklime and about ¼ pt. of turpentine. Paint this on thickly and well dredge over with fine sand. The wood will then be found non-absorbent and, if necessary, washable.

Concrete Floors.—When, for the before-mentioned reasons, a floor independent of the ground is necessary, and it is desired to give it a concrete finish, the floor may normally be made by placing the boards with a space of about ¼ in. between them, and covering with concrete made as follows: Take about three bucketfuls of clean gravel with the stones not larger than a sparrow's egg, and thoroughly mix in with this a little less than half a bucketful of portland cement, or a little more of thoroughly slaked hydraulic lime. Turn the dry material over with a shovel two or three times, then sprinkle with a rose watering-can, and again turn over with the shovel until the concrete is wetted and mixed throughout without being sodden. Now spread it over the boards, levelling off as evenly as possible with the back of the shovel, and allow to dry; then take two pailfuls of clean sand and half a pailful of portland cement. Mix this together as before, wet the surface of the first layer of concrete, then spread on the second layer, and level off with a trowel.

The Framing.—Practically any sizes of wood which are obtainable can be employed for the main con-

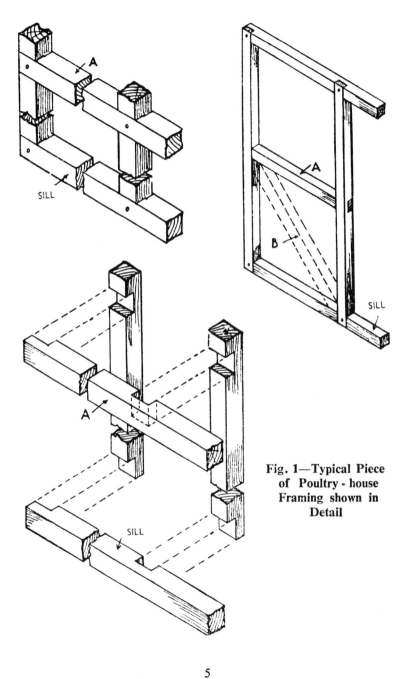

Fig. 1—Typical Piece
of Poultry - house
Framing shown in
Detail

5

struction, these sizes ranging from 2 ins. by 1 in. to about 3 ins. by 3 ins., and the wood normally some variety of deal or fir. If very small sizes are used, the parts must be close together in order to obtain the requisite rigidity, while with heavier material, naturally, fewer posts, etc., are necessary. Generally speaking, 2 ins. by 2 ins. is a very convenient size for all ordinary cases, although the sills at the bottom of a structure can sometimes be 3 ins. or 4 ins. by 2 ins. with advantage. In such a case the uprights might be tenoned into the sill; but for most purposes it will be sufficient to " halve " the whole of the framing together as shown by Fig. 1. The uprights should not be much more than 3 ft. 6 ins. apart, and a middle rail A will generally be necessary where the framing exceeds 5 ft. in height.

Obviously rigidity is imparted when boarding is nailed across the framing either vertically or horizontally; but it may occasionally be found advisable to add stiffness by the introduction of a sloping " brace " as at B, fitted tightly in position and well nailed.

Some typical units of framing are shown by Fig. 2. Their uprights must, of course, be spaced out to suit the size and position of any door or window openings. In the case of an end it is usually as well to make the sloping top portion all in one with the lower part, as at C and D, rather than in two pieces, as is sometimes done. The only extra joints required are simple oblique halvings similar to that at E.

Structures of the type under consideration, while all of a comparatively temporary character, may be classed for the present purpose as either permanent or movable. Permanent houses will perhaps be more heavily constructed, and put together without much regard for easy subdivision into convenient units, while movable ones will be composed of suitable sections connected together by means of a number of $\frac{1}{4}$-in. bolts and washers (Fig. 3), and screws, the latter being oiled before insertion in order to facilitate withdrawal. In any event, however, the construction of several units makes for easier working, and greater strength at the angles where it is most required. The principle involved is to frame up each side separately and to fix them all together as in Fig. 4, either permanently or, as before mentioned, with bolts or screws, two of the former being sufficient at each corner.

In many cases the uprights will be square in section instead of oblong; but the principle will be the same, and in fact the bolting will then be rather simpler to arrange. Usually it will be found best to make the longer side butt against the shorter, as at F, thus reducing its total length by about 4 ins., which will help to make it easier to construct and handle. If, however, the sides are inconveniently long, there is nothing to prevent each one being in two or more portions, bolted together as before, but in a straight line on plan instead of at right angles. Of course, more elaborate work, such as the tenoning of the various rails into one corner-post from two sides, can be indulged in by the expert; but the above simple methods are sufficient for all practical purposes.

Foundations.—Small houses in dry, sheltered positions can be merely bedded on the ground, or, preferably, on a base of ashes or bricks. Where some degree of fixing is advisable they can be nailed or spiked down to the tops of substantial pegs or pointed stakes driven into the ground. Another method is to frame the work up with the posts projecting downwards into the ground, perhaps surrounding them with a little concrete. This course, however, is not recommended, as the buried ends are bound to rot in time, even if well tarred or creosoted—a precaution very necessary for all woodwork in contact with earth.

Larger structures can be very suitably spiked or screwed to fairly heavy lengths of wood used as sleepers laid across the site, these giving ample weight and security. Probably, however, the most satisfactory method for a large house is to prepare a ground sill of the required size, and of at least 4-ins. by 2-ins. wood halved together at the angles. This is bedded quite level on the ground and secured either by its own weight, long pointed pegs in the ground, or the use of concrete, and on it the framing is erected as in Fig. 5, fixing being obtained by the use of bolts or long screws through the sills of the framing. If a boarded floor is required, in such a case it can be laid

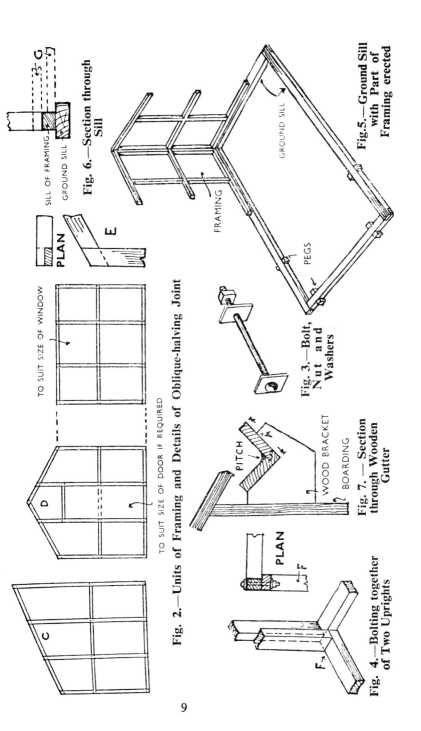

SILL OF FRAMING

GROUND SILL

Fig. 6.—Section through Sill

PLAN

E

Fig. 3.—Bolt, Nut and Washers

GROUND SILL

FRAMING

PEGS

Fig.5.—Ground Sill with Part of Framing erected

TO SUIT SIZE OF WINDOW

TO SUIT SIZE OF DOOR IF REQUIRED

D

Fig. 2.—Units of Framing and Details of Oblique-halving Joint

C

PITCH

WOOD BRACKET

BOARDING

Fig. 7.— Section through Wooden Gutter

PLAN

F

F

Fig. 4.—Bolting together of Two Uprights

9

either on the ground sill or the smaller one as at G in Fig. 6, and supported at intervals of about 2 ft. 6 ins. on suitable small bearers or " plates " bedded on the ground layer.

There are more elaborate forms of foundation in which brick bases are used, or the woodwork is held down by bolts bedded in concrete. The professional poultry farmer may, or may not, consider them an advantage, but they are, generally speaking, unsuited to the amateur, and are open to the grave objection of constituting the whole of the work a landlord's fixture, for which reason houses that cannot be removed without injury to the ground or premises must be avoided. This means that concrete should not be used in any form on rented premises unless some undertaking in writing can be obtained from the landlord renouncing any claim to such a structure on the understanding that all traces of it are cleared away and made good at the end of the tenancy.

The Roof.—The roof should not be of too flat a slope, or it may retain rainwater. Its function is to throw the water clear of the house, and for this purpose it should project at least 3 ins. on all sides, and more if possible on the front. Extensive roofs should have eaves-gutters either of the ordinary metal type or of wood delivering into small tanks or butts. A suitable wooden gutter is shown in Fig. 7, and can be supported on simple brackets. The internal angle should be thickly waterproofed with pitch.

Dealing next with the rafters to support the roof-boarding, it should be understood that these are most effective in their depth, on which they depend for resistance against bending or sagging; that is, they should be placed on edge. Thus a piece $2\frac{1}{2}$ ins. deep and $1\frac{1}{2}$ ins. wide, placed so [], would make a rather better rafter than another 2 ins. by 2 ins. placed, of course, so ⊓, although containing less wood, the respective cross-sectional areas being 3 and $4\frac{3}{4}$ sq. ins. Either of these sizes would suffice in ordinary circumstances for lengths not exceeding 6 ft., above which 3 ins. by 2 ins. would be better, of course, placed so [], but it is sometimes conveniently possible to make them efficient over a longer span by means of small sloping struts as at H in Fig. 8. The spacing will depend on the boarding employed. If this is 1 in. thick it will span 3 ft. 6 ins. or more with ease; but $\frac{5}{8}$-in. wood should be supported at about 2-ft. intervals.

Lean-to Roofs.—A short lean-to roof can usually be dealt with as at J in Fig. 8, with one or more horizontal bearers or " purlins " dropped into slots formed with cut blocks at the ends as at K, unless it be preferred to notch them into the top end rails as at L. As indicated, it is desirable that the ends should come very near one of the intermediate uprights.

A neat mode of fixing such a purlin would be to employ plain metal angle-brackets screwed in position. With an arrangement on the lines of Fig. 8 the boarding would be fixed with its edges running up the slope:

B

but for a long roof not easily spanned with one timber ordinary rafters as in Fig. 9 should be used, notched or " birdsmouthed " over the heads of the front and back framing as at M.   When working on this system, the sloping tops of the ends should finish above the heads of the front and back framing as at N, in order to line with the tops of the rafters, across which the boarding should be fixed horizontally.

Span Roofs.—With span or ridged roofs similar alternatives present themselves.   One or more horizontal timbers can be used on each slope, as at O in Fig. 10, in conjunction with a ridge either as at P or Q. An alternative method is to use a ridge to take the nailed top ends of rafters as in Fig. 11, their lower ends being birdsmouthed as before.   It is, of course, necessary to arrange all top surfaces of rafters in the same planes as the slope of the ends, in order that the boarding may be fixed properly.   A good way in which to fix the ends of the ridge is shown in Fig. 12, and another in Fig. 13.   The first shows the rafters butted and notched at the apex to suit the ridge which is also notched, while the small " collar " piece is spiked across the rafters to hold them in position as at R.   In the other method the rafters are butted without notching, and the collar is fixed at the right level to suit the bottom of the ridge.   In each case extra strength might be obtained by means of a metal angle screwed on as shown in Fig. 13.   Ridges should be about 4 ins. or 5 ins. by 1 in.

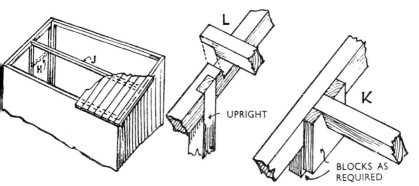

Fig. 8. —Small Lean-to Roof, with Detail of Purlin

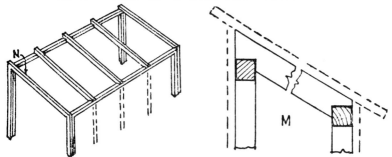

Fig. 9.—Lean-to Roof with Rafters

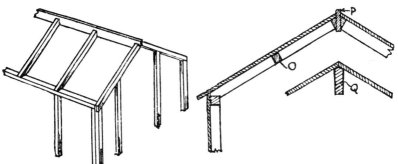

Fig. 11.—Span Roof with
Ridge and Rafters

Fig. 10.—Span Roof with
Purlin

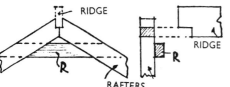

Figs. 12 and 13.—Methods of Securing Ridge at Ends of Roof

13

For wide or long span roofs an occasional " tie," secured against the feet of the rafters as at s in Fig. 14 is advantageous when the headroom is sufficient. This figure also explains another method of constructing a span roof, which is to prepare and erect the four sides in the ordinary way, and on them to erect triangles or " trusses " at intervals. These each consist of two rafters as in Fig. 14, connected by the tie s and a collar at the top as shown, and are used without any ridge, the boarding serving to keep them in the proper relationship to each other.

Boarded, Felted and Tarred Roofs.—The roof boarding itself, if suitably fixed, can be made to stiffen the framing very considerably. It should, if possible, be of the tongued variety, as it is sure to shrink a little, and will in nine cases out of ten be covered with felt. This material is conveniently light and cheap, but requires careful fixing and occasional tarring. It should be stout, well lapped at the joints, closely nailed, and turned well over the edges of the boarding, which may be suitably rounded as shown in Fig. 7. In exposed situations it should be further secured by means of small wood strips, equally spaced out and nailed on to it at short intervals as in Fig. 15. These also tend to improve the appearance of a felted roof. The roof may be made watertight with tar and felt in the following manner: To 1 gal. of tar add a piece of pitch as large as a coconut. It is not expensive. Dissolve in the tar by heat, and apply to the roof hot.

If a special tarring brush is not available, a black-lead brush, nailed or tied to a broom-handle, forms a serviceable instrument, enabling the work to be done very easily on a warm day. If the tar becomes thick, heat the bucket again. Remember that tar soon boils over, so that when on the fire it should be watched. Sand can be sprinkled on the soft tar if such a finish is desired.

Corrugated-iron Roofs.—Another simple roofing is corrugated-iron, the galvanizing of which should be protected with paint or tar. It tends to make the interior hot in summer and cold in winter, but this can be obviated by laying it on thin boarding. It can be obtained in any required sizes; but the rafters should be spaced out to suit the widths of the sheets. Nails with washers are necessary for fixing, and iron ridges can be obtained when required.

Special Roofs.—There are also various special roofing materials such as asbestos, bitumen sheeting, etc., normally to be considered. Ventilation must be good in such cases. Often felt over wire-netting is employed and straw thatch on wire-netted supports.

Weather-boarding Roofs.—Lastly, there is exposed boarding of the feather-edged or " weather " type. This makes a very presentable roof, but should have a pronounced slope in order to prevent any lodgment of rain. It is essential that it be kept in good condition by means of painting or coating with some reliable preservative. Weather-boarding is usually of the plain or rebated sections shown in Fig. 16. In any case the boarding for a removable house can, if preferred, be made up into sections for easy fixing by means of ledges across the underside, just as a ledged door would be made.

Covering the Sides.—For this purpose, corrugated-iron, asbestos sheeting, tongued boarding, or weather-boarding are suitable. It is very desirable that the house be free from draughts such as would result from defective sides. The joints should be vertical, and the end-grain at the bottom kept clear of the ground if possible, as it is comparatively absorbent. The boarding can be fixed permanently to the sides, even if these are contrived to come apart for transport on occasion, as it will not interfere with such an arrangement.

Other possible materials are rustic-work, felt over wire-netting, straw bundles, timber substitutes, and three-ply, which would be very suitable for internal partitions.

Painting, Lime-whiting, Tarring, etc.—All external woodwork might be given two coats of a good preservative, creosote, tar, or paint. Care should be taken that these applications are renewed periodically, so that the woodwork may not be allowed to deteriorate.

For the interiors of houses, coops, etc., limewash is generally advocated; but a coat of Stockholm tar mixed with turpentine and creosote is sometimes favoured and does not rub off. A house so treated should be washed over twice a year with water to which some disinfectant has been added. The slots into which perches lodge should be frequently dressed with paraffin or creosote to prevent the accumulation of red mites.

Before carrying out a re-whitening of a poultry-house the soiled walls should be washed down with a strong solution of soda, soft soap and water. This done, the inside woodwork should be well sprayed with a strong disinfectant. An ordinary garden syringe or sprayer suits the purpose admirably. Special care should be taken to send the disinfectant well into all seams, joints and crevices. When the wood is dry again, treat thoroughly with a coat of limewash made as follows: Put $\frac{1}{2}$ bushel of quicklime into a water-tight barrel, pour on boiling water until covered 4 ins. or 5 ins. deep, and stir until the lime is slaked. Some dissolve in water 1 lb. of common salt and 2 lb. of sulphate of zinc, and mix the solution well into the lime. This causes the limewash to harden on the woodwork. Stir well, and add more water if necessary to give the consistency of cream, and apply with a whitewash brush. The ends of perches, as already stated, should be dipped in paraffin oil or creosoted to prevent them harbouring insect pests. Limewash makes for light interiors.

Outside Feeding Troughs.—These can often be conveniently attached to poultry houses, etc., and consist merely of any ordinary form of trough placed or suspended under a series of apertures through which the birds may feed without interfering one with another. As shown in Fig. 17, these holes can very suitably be circular and of about 2 ins. or $2\frac{1}{2}$ ins. in diameter. The illustration also indicates a hinged flap which serves, when down, to close the holes, and when raised (by means of a small chain) acts as a shade or shelter to the contents of the trough.

A slotted grid is an alternative, or a pivoted trough may be preferred. Food and water containers can rest in an outside box with hinged lid.

Ventilating Ridge.—When a span- or ridge-roof is adopted, it is possible to incorporate with it a simple but quite efficient form of ventilator on the lines of Fig. 18. Here the roof-boarding stops short of the actual apex, leaving a space about 4 ins. or 5 ins. across. This is covered in with two boards mitred together and kept $1\frac{1}{2}$ ins. above the main slopes by means of blocks at intervals, as at A. With this arrangement, whenever there is any wind at all some is practically certain to enter at one side and pass out at the other, thus creating an updraught and preventing stagnation inside the house. Even without any wind this open ridge forms an outlet for the rising heated air without causing any draughts.

For ordinary weather there should also be plenty of side ventilation; but while such openings should be capable of complete or partial closure, or be baffled,

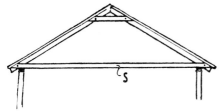

Fig. 14.—Span Roof with Rafters
and Tie

Fig. 15.—Strips on
Felted Roof

Fig. 16.—Types of
Weather Boarding

Fig. 17.—Extending
Feeding Trough

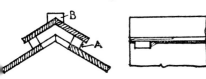

Fig. 18.—Ventilating Ridge

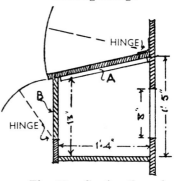

Fig. 19.—Section through
External Nest Box

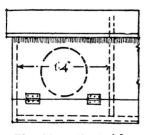

Fig. 20. — Outside
Elevation of External
Nest Box

Fig. 22.—Glass Puttied
in Rebate

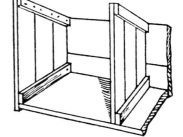

Fig. 21.—View of External Nest Box

19

this ridge ventilator can be left always open. The joint between the two boards at the extreme top can be covered with felt or with a fillet worked to fit over the joint as at B, and the top boards should overlap the lower ones at least 2 ins. in order to exclude driving rain. Ridge-caps can be flat and may be raised or lowered according to season.

Outside Nesting Boxes.—In many houses, fixed nest-boxes are projected from the sides, the advantages being that more internal space is available for scratching purposes, and the eggs are very much more convenient for collection, unless a design having fixed internal nests and inspection doors (see later pages) is adopted. The boxes are kept clear of the ground and arranged with their entrances screened from the daylight as much as possible. Inside the house an 8-inch fly-up board is fitted which the layers use before entering the compartment to lay.

They can for all ordinary purposes be quite satisfactorily constructed, as in Figs. 19, 20 and 21. The first of these gives the sizes and shows a sloping top on cross-ledges A, overhanging a little at the lower edge. When the boxes are near the ground this sloping top should be hinged in one piece to lift up from all the three or more compartments it covers at once, as a separate top to each would entail joints likely to admit rain. For the same reason it may suitably be hinged with a continuous strip of leather; or metal hinges may be adopted.

When the boxes are well above the ground (as in the case of a roost having a covered run arranged under it), a hinged front, as at B (Fig. 19), is less inconvenient for access than if at a lower level, and may be adopted in lieu of the hinged top, which would then be entirely fixed, the other serving quite well both for cleaning purposes and for collecting the eggs. It can be continuous or divided into separate doors for the different nests; but it is often advisable to fit such doors with staples and padlocks against thieves, in which case one long door will be found both cheaper to fit and certainly easier for inspection.

Fig. 21 clearly explains the construction of a range of outside next-boxes, the upright divisions being ledged as shown, and held together by the bottom boarding and that of the top or front (whichever it is decided to fix). When completed it can be fixed in position against the house by means of stout fillets screwed to its edges and to the boarding, or with the help of small metal angles. The lid can pass into the house a little to prevent rain entering. The most usual means of access for the fowls is a circular hole about 3 ins. above the floor of the nest as dotted in Fig. 20, this cutting away least boarding and keeping the interior fairly dark. It is, of course, perfectly easy to adapt to external boxes any of the trapping devices for egg-recording the layers.

Doors.—These can be of the simplest description, and it is an easy matter to produce a ledged and braced door as in Fig. 23. It consists of a rectangle of **V**-jointed boarding about 2 ft. by 5 ft. 6 ins., held together with two horizontal cross-pieces or " ledges " and a sloping " brace," the whole being secured with long nails driven right through both thicknesses and turned over at their points.

If a pane of glass is desired the door can be modified as in Fig. 24, an opening being cut in the upper part

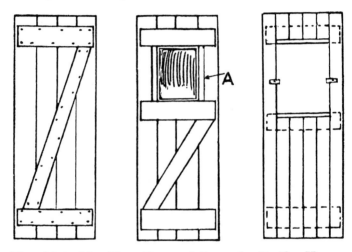

Figs. 23 to 25.—Three Types of Doors for Poultry Houses

and ledges fixed $\frac{1}{2}$ in. above and below this, leaving a rebate into which the glass can be puttied top and bottom. A similar rebate is formed at each side by the addition of two small vertical strips as at A in Figs. 22 and 24.

A third type of door is shown by Fig. 25, and has a larger opening, rebates being again formed at top and bottom by the overlapping of the ledges. On the inside, the opening would be filled in with wire mesh, while a plain wooden shutter would be made to fit into the opening on the outside when required, and be held in place by a couple of wooden turn-buckles.

In certain cases it may be found advantageous to have inside an ordinary door a lighter one, consisting simply of a wood frame covered with wire-netting, so that light and air may be admitted to the fullest extent without allowing the birds to escape. This frame may be hinged to open inwards, or kept entirely separate and only placed in position when actually required.

Sills, etc.—Where projecting sills are shown under windows, etc., in the following designs, they can be

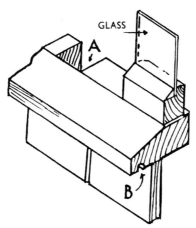

Fig. 26.—Detail of Door Sill, Glass, etc.

merely planted on the face of the framing, but a better plan would be to arrange them as in Fig. 26. Here the sill takes the form of a flat rail of about 4 ins. by 2 ins., forming part of the general framing, and notched where required to fit round the uprights as at A and sloped on the top as shown. It should also be throated as at B in order to prevent water reaching the boarding under. The casements used can be of quite the ordinary type and about $1\frac{1}{2}$ ins. thick.

Designs for Houses.—This chapter has been concerned very largely with constructional principles and standard details. In later chapters will be found a large number of designs for different types of houses —range, semi-intensive, and intensive—and in those designs can be incorporated a number of the details and principles that have been explained in this chapter. In many cases, later chapters will be found to present some alternative methods of construction.

CHAPTER II

Troughs and Fountains

TROUGHS—Suitable troughs can be easily made to the exact size and style required. Various types are illustrated in this chapter, and can be adapted in size to suit chicks or full-grown birds. They can also, if desired, be divided into compartments for the different kinds of food, and wire guards can be fitted.

Feeding receptacles must be of a shape that is not easily overturned. A useful trough is shown by Fig. 27. The ends are triangular pieces of wood, and the trough proper is formed by two plain boards mitred and fixed together **V**-fashion, as in Fig. 28. The two upper points of the ends are connected by a wooden bar with a sharp edge on top, making it awkward for the birds to perch on it, and effectually preventing them from treading on their food. This bar can be arranged to turn round as a spinner for the same purpose.

The construction is essentially simple, consisting only of butt joints, nailed or screwed through the end pieces, and the length would be adjusted to suit the number of birds to be catered for.

Another easily made trough is explained by Fig. 29, and the section (Fig. 30), which gives suggested sizes for the use of full-grown birds. It would be made in the same way as the V-trough, of wood about $\frac{1}{2}$ in.

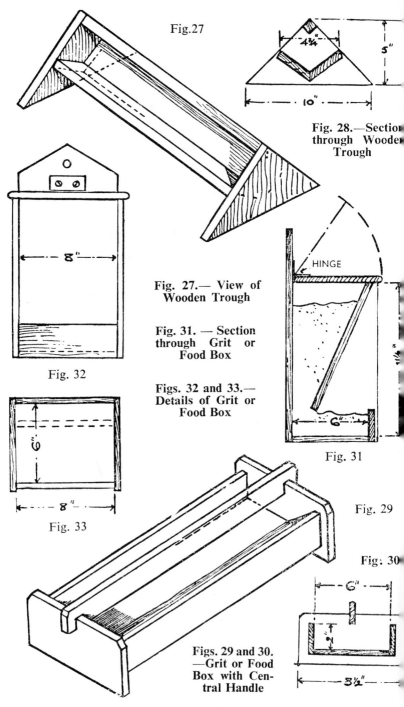

Fig.27

Fig. 28.—Section through Wooden Trough

Fig. 27.— View of Wooden Trough

Fig. 31. — Section through Grit or Food Box

Figs. 32 and 33.— Details of Grit or Food Box

Fig. 32

Fig. 33

Fig. 31

HINGE

Fig. 29

Fig: 30

Figs. 29 and 30. —Grit or Food Box with Central Handle

26

thick, and the central bar at the top is intended to be notched to fit over the ends. If preferred, this bar might be made deeper, in order to divide the trough into two distinct longitudinal compartments.

Self-filling Grit Boxes, etc.—A time-saving device consisting of a semi-automatic box primarily intended for the supply of grit and oyster-shell (which should always be available to the birds), but equally suitable for dry mash or pellets, is shown by Figs. 31 to 34. For grit, etc., the sizes given would be found fully adequate; but for dry foodstuffs the reservoir might be increased to any reasonable extent, and it could also be widened to include compartments for food, and grit side by side. A reference to the section in

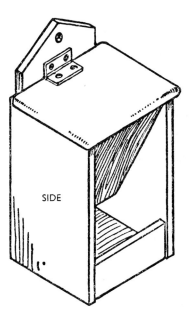

Fig. 34.—General View of Box for Grit, Dry Mash or Pellets

Fig. 31 will make the working quite clear. At the bottom there is a shallow trough fed by a sloping compartment or " hopper," into which the material is filled by means of a hinged flap at the top. As the trough is emptied by the birds a corresponding amount filters through from the hopper, and the trough is thereby maintained at a reasonably well-filled level. A wide lip round the trough will prevent waste of food. The box can be hung in any desired position, and the reservoir increased in capacity to any extent, as previously mentioned.

The article can be very simply made by nailing a thin back, base, sloping front, and bottom strip (all seen in section in Fig. 31) between two square side pieces as in Fig. 34. The back projects at the top for hanging purposes, and a lid is hinged to it as shown; while, if desired, a small loose flap can be kept at hand in order to cover up or control the supply of food, etc., in the trough when required. Food must have an easy flow and all waste be avoided.

Metal Troughs.—Anyone accustomed to the manipulation of sheet metal and solder could easily produce some neat and hygienic troughs for food and water. The one shown in Fig. 35 is figured to sizes suitable for chicks, and is easily cleaned out by washing under a tap. The trough is covered by a guard of loops, and the chicks feed by eating between the spaces. A division can be soldered across the centre as shown for a variety of food. Fig. 36 shows a full-size trough suitable for an intensive house where a pen of birds could be fed with almost any diet. It is 20 ins. long by 7 ins. wide, and in the centre is fixed a partition. Its wire divisions, with the centre partition, prevent one greedy fowl from appropriating all the best part of a feeding trough. Even simpler in construction is

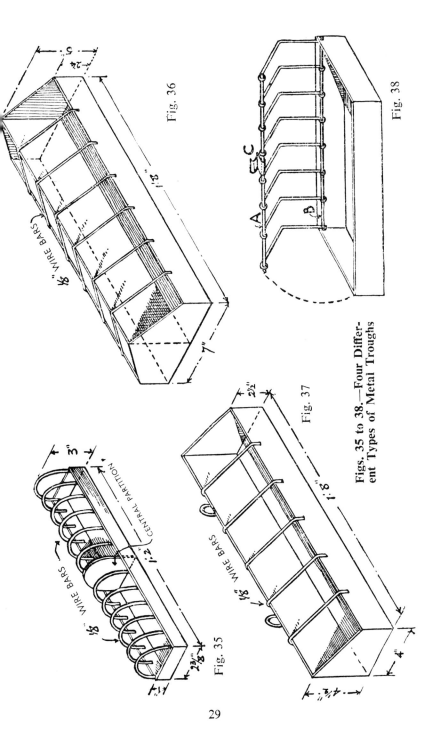

1/8" WIRE BARS

Fig. 36

Fig. 38

C

A

B

Figs. 35 to 38.—Four Different Types of Metal Troughs

2½"

1'8"

4"

1/8" WIRE BARS

Fig. 37

3"

CENTRAL PARTITION

WIRE BARS

1'2"

2 3/8"

1'4"

1/8"

Fig. 35

29

the trough shown in Fig. 37, which is specially adapted, by reason of its shape and the two hooks shown, for hanging on the wall inside a pen, or in other suitable positions.

These troughs are firm and easily cleaned; but it is often considered an improvement to arrange the wire guards to lift up, so as to afford unhindered access to the interior. This is a tedious matter in the case of the small sizes; but for larger ones it can easily be accomplished as shown by Figs. 38 and 39. The troughs there illustrated form two other examples of easy sheet-metal construction, suitable for any desired size or height. In Fig. 38 the short wire guards are bent, and looped tightly round a couple of stout longitudinal wires A and B. The latter is made sufficiently long for its ends to project through small holes in the upright ends of the trough, as indicated. This forms a species of hinge, and the wire A is a trifle shorter than the inside of the trough; so that when closed it falls just below the top edge of the front, to which it is sufficiently secured by means of a clip composed of a strip of tin, bent and soldered in position as at C. The wirework must obviously be completed ready for insertion before the trough is finally fixed together.

Fig. 39 shows another trough also fitted with a hinged guard, the bars of which are in this case semi-circular. Otherwise the arrangement is very much as before. It will be noted that when an even number

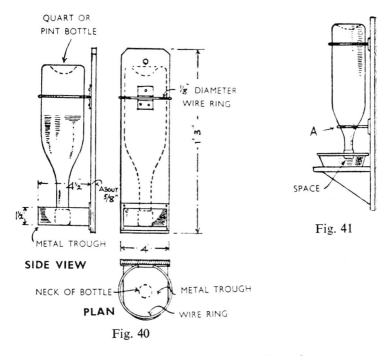

QUART OR
PINT BOTTLE

⅛" DIAMETER
WIRE RING

1' 3"

4½"

ABOUT
⅝"

1½"

METAL TROUGH

SIDE VIEW

4"

NECK OF BOTTLE · · METAL TROUGH

PLAN

WIRE RING

Fig. 40

A →

SPACE

Fig. 41

Figs. 40 and 41.—Bottle Drinking Fountains

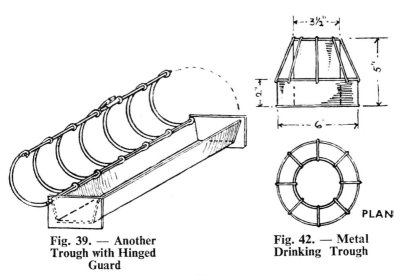

3½"

5"

2"

6"

PLAN

**Fig. 39. — Another
Trough with Hinged
Guard**

**Fig. 42. — Metal
Drinking Trough**

31

of divisions is made the little clip, intended to spring over the front edge when closed, cannot be fixed quite in the centre of the length. With metalwork of this character it should be observed that all sharp angles and edges are sufficiently rounded off, and the ends of the various wires rendered harmless to the birds.

Drinking Fountains.—Special drinking fountains are of great advantage. If a vessel of water is placed on the floor of an intensive house, dirt or litter is scratched in to foul the water, which is often upset, and the birds walk in it, wetting the house. Fig. 40 shows a bottle fountain, which can be hung on the wall or partition above the floor, so as not to diminish floor space. It is always clean, and there is no risk of its being upset. It will be seen to consist of a simple wood back, holed for hanging purposes, having at its base a sheet-metal container $1\frac{1}{2}$ ins. deep. Inverted in this is a suitable bottle, supported by a wire ring clipped to the back as shown. This bottle acts as a reservoir, from which the container is fed, the water in the latter being maintained at a constant level until the bottle is emptied. While the amount of water exposed at a time is sufficient for drinking purposes, there is no risk of the objections previously mentioned being experienced, and yet no fear of the water supply running short. Be it noted that in practice the bottle does not rest on the bottom of the metal container, but is raised about 1 in. or $1\frac{1}{2}$ ins., and the water will keep at that depth (see Fig. 41), the additional wire A being probably ncessary.

Another type of drinker is shown in Fig. 42. This is all metal. The wires depicted in the plan prevent the chicken from getting into the water, and the whole could be very easily produced if some tins of about the sizes indicated can be incorporated in the work.

Tinplate is unsuitable for making water containers on account of the readiness with which it rusts. The commencement of this rusting may readily be seen if a tinplate receptacle is filled with clean water and allowed to remain, say, for a few days. This is probably due to the fact that iron and tin have very little affinity to each other, consequently the surface of the tinplate is usually imperfectly coated during the process of tinning in the production of the tinplate.

Zinc is without doubt a more suitable metal; but the drawback to its use is its higher cost. If metal troughs are made it can be safely said that light galvanized iron will be found more suitable, especially in point of durability.

CHAPTER III

Inside Nesting-boxes and Trap-nests

INSIDE NESTING-BOXES.—Nest-boxes are often of the packing-case order and therefore very readily replaced. A simple type is shown in Fig. 43, about 15 ins. or 16 ins. wide and deep inside, with a little more for the height, a vertical board being provided at the bottom of the front to keep the nesting material together. A triangular nest-box (Figs. 44 and 45) is occasionally useful, and can be inserted into any corner, without taking up much room. It can be built up of boarding nailed to fillets at the corners, and held together by the boarded top and bottom.

A combined nest-box and perch is shown in Fig. 46, and gives a simple idea that may be used; it is excellent for bantams. By means of a couple of plain uprights secured to the sides of an ordinary nesting-box, a length of perch can be supported at any desired level. It might be loosely socketed into the uprights.

Sitting-boxes.—Sitting-boxes should be at least comparatively dark. A typical sitting-box is illustrated in Fig. 47, and is furnished with two doors. The front one should be hinged so that it can easily be opened, and should have a simple fastener at the top, so that it can be kept closed. Use $\frac{1}{2}$-in. mesh netting, as, if large netting were employed, the newly hatched

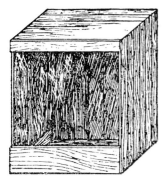

Fig. 43.—Nest-box

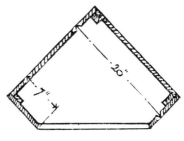

Fig. 44

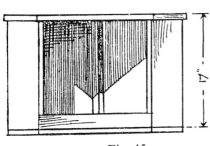

Fig. 45

Figs. 44 and 45.—Corner Nest-box

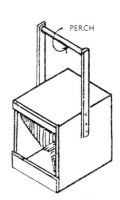

Fig. 46.—Nest-box and Perch

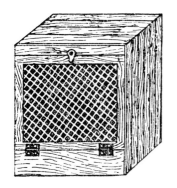

Fig. 47.—Sitting-box

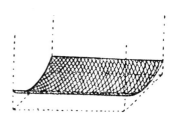

Fig. 48.—Wire Bottom for Sitting-box

35

chickens would fall out of the box through the mesh, and vermin might get through to disturb the sitting hen. The back of the sitting-box forms the other door. It can have a wire-netting (fine mesh) bottom, as this allows the moisture to rise to the eggs, whilst effectively guarding them against vermin. This wire-netting bottom should be concave, from back to front, as in Fig. 48.

Nest-box under Drop-board.—It is simple to arrange movable boxes under the boards and with their secluded entrances away from the front. Assuming such an arrangement, the box shown by Fig. 49 would be found suitable and very easily made. The farther end is the entrance facing the back of the house, while at the nearer end there is a half-door to facilitate the collection of eggs. A board at the bottom will serve as a fly-up.

Hen-trapping Nests.—Where it is required to know the number of eggs laid by a particular hen or to recognize the eggs of each hen, some form of trap-nest is needed. There are many and varied designs, a simple form being shown by Figs. 50 to 52.

When the hen desires to enter the nest-box to lay, she must perforce brush aside and push down the little prop A holding up the drop door B, which then falls, closing the entrance and keeping the hen in until released. When releasing her reset the trap by lifting the prop again into position to hold up the door. The prop is of wire of about $\frac{1}{8}$ in. in diameter.

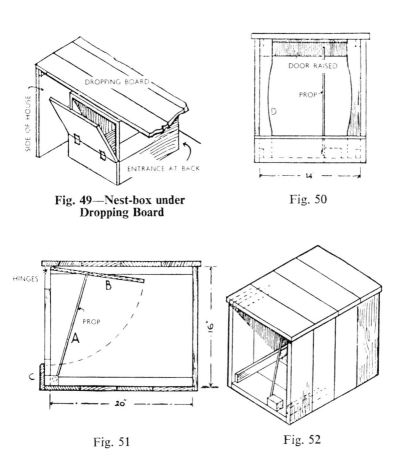

Fig. 49—Nest-box under Dropping Board

Fig. 50

Fig. 51

Fig. 52

Figs. 50 to 52.—Hen-trapping Nest

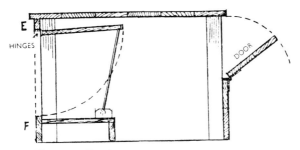

Fig. 53.—Section through another Trap-nest

In making the box allow it a few inches longer than would be otherwise necessary, so as to provide room for the hen to stand or sit, without being struck by the falling door. If made 20 ins. long by 14 ins. wide and 16 ins. high, this will be all correctly arranged.

The door should be sufficiently long to allow it to rest against the inside of the cross ledge c nailed at the bottom of the box front. Thus it cannot be opened outwards by the hen from within, and so she cannot release herself. The little wire prop is secured with a nail or screw to a small block as shown in Fig. 51, and should be very loosely held, so that it cannot stick fast or catch. When the door is down the prop will be lost amongst the straw, etc., of the nest. The door should be made as light and gentle in action as possible, so as not to hurt or startle the hen, while the box itself should be of $\frac{3}{4}$-in. deal boarding, put together by means of fillets at the inside corners, as dotted in Fig. 50. The top boarding might overhang a little as shown, to facilitate lifting, and it will be best if the whole or a part of the back be arranged to open. Fig. 52 shows the box complete, with the exception of the shaped side pieces D (Fig. 50), and the board across the bottom seen in section at c in Fig. 51.

Of course, the bottom boarding could be omitted from the preceding example if preferred, as has been done in another type of trap-nest shown by Figs. 53 to 55, and which was very popular at one time. Here the bird is more completely clear of the falling door;

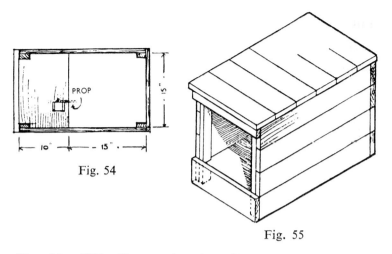

Fig. 54

Fig. 55

Figs. 54 and 55.—Hen-trapping Nest. (See also Fig. 53, p. 37.)

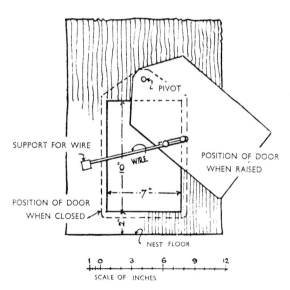

Fig. 56.—Trap-door for ordinary Nest-box

but the box is correspondingly longer. There is a sort of boarded platform leading to the nest, and the prop is arranged in such a position, and with its end so near the edge, that the slightest touch suffices to release the raised door. Fig. 55 shows the trap ready set, and explains the position of the boards E and F (Fig. 53), which are nailed across the front of the box.

Fig. 56 shows another early type of trap-nest. It is easy to set and its fall makes no noise.

Make a front, of any wood, to an ordinary nest-box, and cut an opening as shown. Make the door out of thin wood, 8 ins. by 13 ins., and fasten the top with a screw as a pivot. The wire seen across the opening is flattened at one end and nailed to the door, a fixture. A small block serving as a support or rest is fixed where shown, and this keeps the door from falling down. To enter the nest, the fowl presses in under the wire, lifting up its loose end, causing the thin movable front to fall into place behind her, shutting the bird inside. The outer door can easily be cut out of tin-plate. Release the bird when she has laid, and set the nest again.

Nests for Egg-eaters.—Occasionally a hen will develop the habit of eating eggs. The nest illustrated by Figs. 57 to 59 is designed to prevent the eggs laid from being eaten. This is accomplished by fixing a shelf G in the nest-box about 3 ins. up from the box bottom. It should slope downwards to the rear sufficiently to

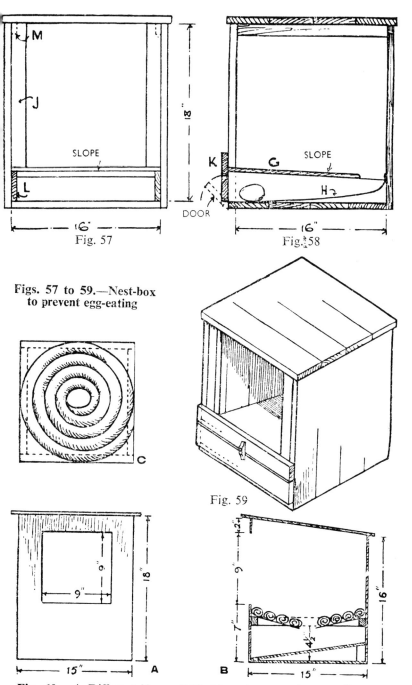

M

J

SLOPE

L

18"

16"

Fig. 57

DOOR

K

G

SLOPE

H

16"

Fig. 58

Figs. 57 to 59.—Nest-box
to prevent egg-eating

C

Fig. 59

9"

9"

18"

15"

A

12"

9"

7"

4"

16"

15"

B

Fig. 60.—A Different Type of Nest-box to prevent egg-eating

allow the egg to roll gently back until it drops through a gap left for the purpose. This is arranged by making the shelf 2 ins. narrower than the depth of the box and nailing it in place flush with the front. The egg falls on a piece of canvas H tacked to the back and bottom of the box, and sloped the reverse way to the wooden shelf. This causes the egg to roll to the front of the box to the position shown in Fig. 58. The small door, shown closed, keeps it from rolling out, and to prevent possible cracking of the egg has a strip of thick cloth or felt tacked inside it. The tacks should be omitted from where the egg must cushion, being strictly confined to the top and bottom edges. By unbuttoning and opening the door, the egg may be removed as convenient. The box should measure about 18 ins. high by 15 ins. or 16 ins. square. The side strips J at the front are $1\frac{1}{2}$ ins. wide, and the cross ledge K 2 ins. The door is secured by hinges at the bottom and a button at the top, and the shelf G is supported on slightly tapering strips fixed against the sides as at L. These strips, together with the top ones as at M, also serve to hold the boarded sides together. The back of the nest can be made to open if desired, and any form of trap could be fitted to the front.

A different type of nest to prevent egg-eating is shown by Fig. 60, A being a front elevation, B a cross section, and C a plan of the actual nest. This nesting-box is intended for fixing outside the house, a hole

9 ins. square being cut for an entrance. One can well be made of three-ply wood, 15 ins. square and 18 ins. high; but any wood will do. First cut down the back 2 ins. for the sloping roof (cut towards the front for an inside nest to prevent fowls roosting on it). Cut an opening 9 ins. square in the front, leaving 7 ins. at the bottom, and fix two strips of wood with their top edges $4\frac{1}{2}$ ins. from the bottom. Put on a roof, projecting 1 in. all round (three-ply nailed to the battens that were in the top, refixed), and cover with roofing felt or a piece of the tin lining from another tea-chest.

A frame is now to be made an easy fit inside the box, and to rest on the ledges. It should be made of anything about 1 in. by $\frac{3}{4}$ in., and be covered loosely with sacking so that it sags towards the centre about $1\frac{1}{2}$ ins. Cut a hole a little larger than the size of an egg, and sew round with a button-hole stitch to prevent fraying. Get a straw band and sew it with strong twine (or sugar string) spirally (as shown), beginning at the centre and making a nice slope towards the hole. A piece of three-ply wood is cut the size of the inside, having a 2-in. block nailed to the front edge, so that the floor of the nest slopes towards the back. Put a few handfuls of sawdust on this board. The hen lays the egg, which immediately drops through the hole and rolls away out of sight. To collect the eggs arrange a hinged door beneath the nest.

CHAPTER IV

Coops

COOP FOR HEN AND CHICKENS.—The ordinary form of chicken coop is shown in Fig. 61, and a useful size is 2 ft. wide by 1 ft. 10 ins. from front to back, 1 ft. 10 ins. high at the front, and 1 ft. at the back. The shutter is useful to close the front of the coop at night, and it also serves to provide shade during the day. Whenever such shutters are attached to poultry appliances they should always have " strap " or " cross-garnet " hinges similar to those illustrated; for as these shutters are exposed to all weathers, and when open are supported by a chain at one end and by hinges at the other, they always have a tendency to warp or bend in the middle. This is especially so when small hinges are used. Obviously, these shutters must fit close if draughts are to be prevented. Bottoms may or may not be provided for the coops, as preferred.

The upright bars in the front of the coop are so spaced that only the chickens can pass between them, but the centre bar is longer than the others and is not a fixture. This is drawn up when it is desired to set the hen at liberty. When this bar is down its bottom ends fits into a socket.

Some poultry keepers have the bars in front horizontal, as in Fig. 62, instead of vertical. When the bars are vertical, the socket for the bottom end of the centre bar is continually being filled with dust, peat, or straw used in the coop, through the chickens throwing it in all directions. Consequently the attendant has frequently to clear out this socket before the centre bar can be fixed. When the bars are horizontal,

Fig. 61

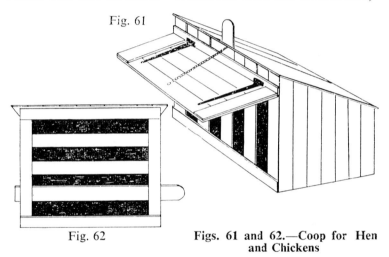

Fig. 62

Figs. 61 and 62.—Coop for Hen and Chickens

the dirt, etc., cannot thus become an impediment, as the movable bar runs through holes cut in each side of the coop.

Coop for Broody Hens.—A few day's confinement in one of these under suitable conditions will generally effect a cure for broodiness. In the coop shown in Fig. 63 the hen is well above ground level, and, being able to see her companions, soon wants to rejoin them. The wire-netted bottom provides a cool sitting place.

The coop may be roughly framed together, as shown by Fig. 67, with deal scantling about $1\frac{1}{2}$ ins. square. If the maker has the necessary tools and skill, the joints should be halved; if not, a few wire nails to hold the joints together until the boards are fixed will do almost as well, as the boards, when in position and nailed, will hold the framing together. A piece of 1 in. mesh wire netting is strained across the top of the middle frame at A in Fig. 64 and secured with small staples. If preferred, the bottom could be formed of thin slats fixed across, with 1 in. spaces between; but either method will largely obviate the necessity for cleaning the interior. Three-quarter-inch matchboarding can be used for covering the sides, back, and top, and the front can be made up with vertical strips of 2 ins. by $\frac{3}{4}$-in. deal as shown in Figs. 65 and 66, the middle strip being passed through a slot in the roof-boards at the top, finishing with a stock or cross-piece as at B in Fig. 69, and secured by means of a hoop-iron or wooden socket at the bottom (C, Figs. 64 and 65), thus providing one of the simplest forms of opening for putting in and taking out the broody hens.

To complete the coop, a feeding-trough about 18 ins. long and 3 ins. by $2\frac{1}{2}$ ins. inside is loosely supported on the projecting ends of the middle rails as at D in Fig. 67, fitting them closely by means of small blocks on its under-side as at E in Fig. 68. Part of this trough can be lined with zinc to form a water-container, or it can be partitioned for water, food and grit containers.

Fig. 63.—Coop for Broody Hen, Isolation or Fattening

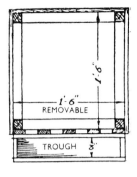

Fig. 66.—Horizontal Section through Coop shown by Fig. 63

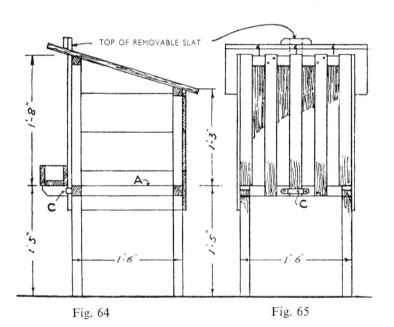

Fig. 64

Fig. 65

Figs. 64 and 65.—Details of Coop.

47

The coop is dimensioned 1 ft. 6 ins. by 1 ft. 6 ins. by 1 ft. 3 ins. to 1 ft. 8 ins. high; but one can increase the sizes somewhat, or make a row of partitioned compartments.

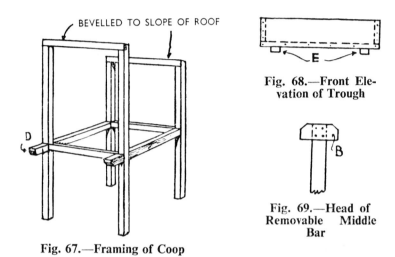

BEVELLED TO SLOPE OF ROOF

Fig. 68.—Front Elevation of Trough

Fig. 69.—Head of Removable Middle Bar

Fig. 67.—Framing of Coop

The slatted or wire floor can be made to slide out for cleaning; some inches beneath the floor a removable droppings-tray can be planned, also to aid hygiene. Such coops have their uses for isolation, also fattening purposes.

CHAPTER V

Some Special Pens, Scratching Sheds, etc.

A PAIR OF COCKEREL PENS.—It is often a great advantage to possess a pen in which a single fowl can be isolated. Indeed, it is often a necessity to confine cockerels to separate houses and runs or they may permanently disfigure each other. The pens may be built singly or in pairs, as shown in Fig. 70, and the top rails at the front and back should project beyond the ends to form handles by means of which they can be easily carried to fresh ground when necessary. The run is framed and covered with 2 in. mesh wire netting, a board partition being used to divide it into the two parts. It will be sufficiently light and strong to lift and move bodily. A mother-hen and her chicks can also be accommodated in such a unit, or a bird being prepared for a show.

To make the pens, about 80 ft. super of $\frac{3}{4}$-in. matchboarding will be required, and in addition about 50 ft. run of $2\frac{1}{2}$-in. by 1 in. deal must be provided for the framing and 60 ft. of $1\frac{1}{2}$-in. square stuff for the runs. Cut two of the framing pieces 7 ft. 3 ins. long, bevel the edges to the rake of the roof, and round off the handles at the ends. Cut two more rails 6 ft. 2 in. long, one for the bottom of the back A (Fig. 73), and the other B (Fig. 71) 1 ft. up in the front. Nail the front boards to the rails B and C, then cut the openings D (Fig. 71) 12 ins. by 8 ins. Next nail on the bottom rails between the openings as shown at E, and fix a light upright fillet in the centre to carry the dividing partition.

The back may then be put together by first nailing on three boards at the centre and half-boards at each end, the spaces between these, at the top and bottom, being filled with 2-in. by $\frac{3}{4}$-in. strips (F and G, Fig. 73), which being narrower than the top and bottom rails will leave $\frac{1}{2}$-in. rebates for the doors. The ends (Fig. 74) may be framed as in Figs. 76 and 77, and boarded, and the sides and ends nailed together. Next fix the partition (Fig. 72) between the two pens, and then the roof can be nailed on, the soundest boards being selected for this.

In making the doors, a board may be sawn down the centre to form the two ledges, and a pair of common butt or **T**-hinges used on each one for hanging. The doors may be fastened with wooden turn-buttons, as shown in Fig. 73, or in some other equally convenient way.

The roof should be covered with felt or other waterproof material, or strips of wood may be nailed over the joints, as shown in Fig. 73. For ventilation a row of 1-in. centre-bit holes should be bored through the front and sides just under the roof.

The run may be made of stuff $1\frac{1}{2}$ in. square; but

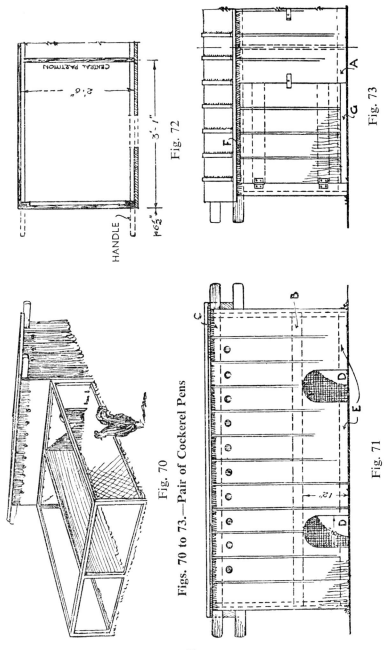

CENTRAL PARTITION

2'6"

3'-1"

6½"

HANDLE

C

Fig. 72

A

G

F

Fig. 73

Fig. 70

B

C

D

E

D

12"

Fig. 71

Figs. 70 to 73.—Pair of Cockerel Pens

51

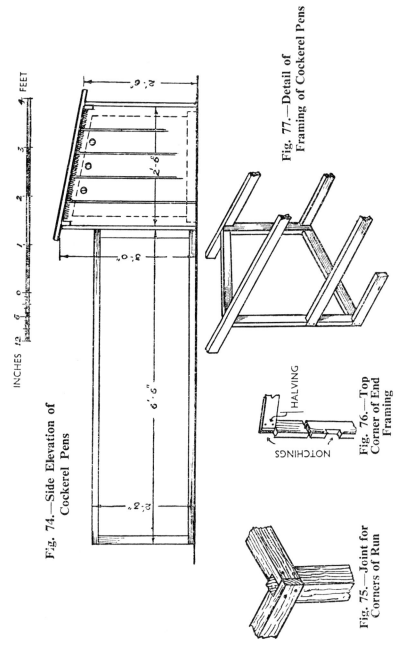

INCHES

FEET

Fig. 74.—Side Elevation of Cockerel Pens

Fig. 77.—Detail of Framing of Cockerel Pens

HALVING

NOTCHINGS

Fig. 76.—Top Corner of End Framing

Fig. 75.—Joint for Corners of Run

the corner posts might be a little stronger, say 2 ins. square, and the corners can be jointed together, as shown in Fig. 75.   The height of the run should be

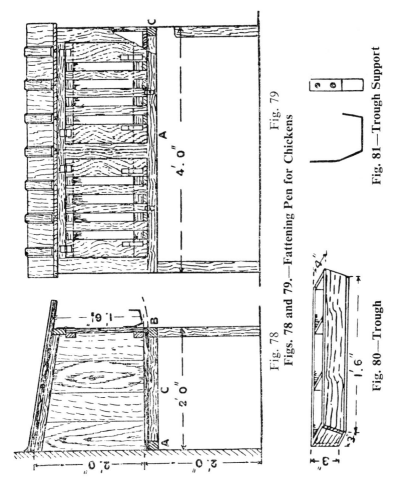

Fig. 79

Figs. 78 and 79.—Fattening Pen for Chickens

Fig. 78

Fig. 81—Trough Support

Fig. 80—Trough

about 27 ins.   If preferred, the sides could be filled in with boarding, and the top arranged to open partially.

Fattening Pens.—To fatten table birds, a finishing

pen always pays for itself. It can be used on occasion
also as a coop for broody hens

Fig. 78 shows a section and Fig. 79 a front elevation
of a simple fattening pen intended to be fixed against
a wall. It is made of matchboarding, and in two
compartments. The legs and framing may be of $1\frac{1}{2}$-in.
by 2-in. deal, and the doors are hinged at the top and
secured at the bottom by means of turn-buttons (see
Fig. 79). The doors lift for cleaning, and a removable
floor is arranged. Some inches beneath the floor, a
tray to catch the droppings is a practical addition.

The roof is of matchboarding, and strips are nailed
over the joints to keep them weather-proof; or the
lot covered with felt. A piece of zinc may be fixed to
the wall at the back to prevent the water running
down behind, and the roof projects about 6 ins. at
the front to keep the feeding-troughs (Fig. 80) dry.
The compartments, or at least the one to hold water,
can be lined with zinc. The troughs are held in
position on the doors by brackets made by 1-in. by
$\frac{1}{8}$-in. hoop-iron bent to fit (see Fig. 81). In making
the pen, the back and front rails A and B (Figs. 78 and
79) would first be framed together with the legs and
the end rails C. The last would then be nailed to the
wall and the bottom fixed. The front and the ends
could then be framed and nailed in position, and a
partition added to divide the two pens. Next the roof
would be put on, and the doors framed together by
simply nailing the ledges across the uprights, and then

hung in position, iron hinges screwed on the face being used.

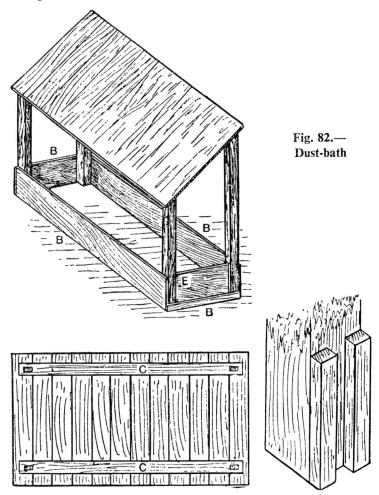

Fig. 82.—
Dust-bath

Fig. 83.—Underside of
Roof

Fig. 84.—Groove for
Sliding Board

Dust-bath.—Health considerations suggest the pre-sence of a dust-bath, a design for which is given in

Fig. 82. Its size depends wholly on the number of fowls housed in the pen. Four 2-in. by 2-in. uprights will be required, those in front being about 2 ft. high, and the rear ones about 3 ft. high. No bottom is necessary, unless it is likely that the dust-bath will have to be moved frequently. The uprights are connected at the bottom by four boards B, and at the top by means of the roof, the underside of which is illustrated at Fig. 83. The cross-rails C which hold the roof-boards together are mortised as indicated, so that tenons on the heads of the uprights can be securely attached to them. The end board E (Fig. 82) slides in grooves on the inner faces of the uprights adjoining it, as illustrated in Fig. 84. The board can then be withdrawn to facilitate removing the ashes by means of a shovel. If no sliding board is made, it is awkward to remove the ashes or dust unless the bath is moved bodily. The bath is shown open on all sides, but, of course, it should be placed against a wall or one side of the pen; otherwise a back will be required.

Scratching Shed.—A want is often experienced for something between a foster-mother and the house and run. The scratching shed illustrated in Figs. 85 and 86 will then be found useful. In its construction is 7-in. by about $\frac{1}{2}$-in. rough boarding. Cut two posts each 1 ft. 9 ins. long by $1\frac{1}{2}$-ins., and two posts each 1 ft. 6 ins. long by $1\frac{1}{2}$ ins. for the corners. Cut off four lengths of 7 ins. by $\frac{1}{2}$ in. each 5 ft. long, and nail one length to the two longer posts to form the bottom

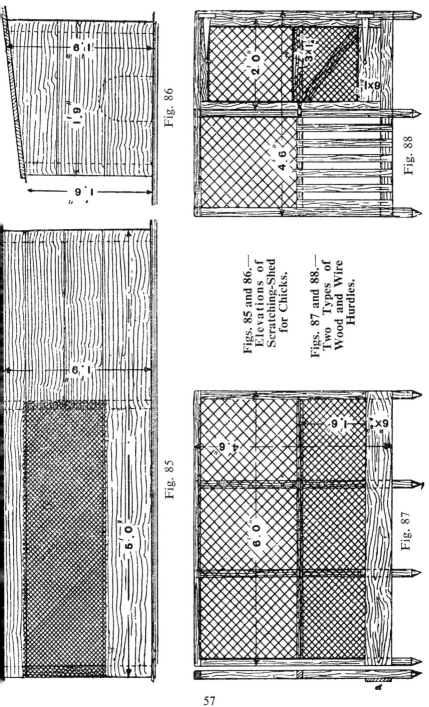

Fig. 86

Fig. 88

Fig. 85

Figs. 85 and 86.— Elevations of Scratching-Shed for Chicks.

Figs. 87 and 88.— Two Types of Wood and Wire Hurdles.

Fig. 87

of the front. Now run a saw down another length, thus making two pieces, one 4 ins. wide and one 3 ins. wide, and nail the 3-in. width to the other end of the longest posts to form the top of the front. Then nail the remaining two lengths to the two shortest posts, and the 4-in. length as well, making 18 ins. in all, and completing the back. Cut off six pieces of board for the two ends each 1 ft. 9 ins. long, and nail them to the posts, cutting the top pieces diagonally between the front and back. A partition must now be prepared for cutting off the sleeping compartment, and this can be made of 1-ft. 8-in. lengths, a couple of battens being nailed on the inside to keep them together, and also to nail the front and back to. Fill up the front of the sleeping compartment, when it will be ready for flooring. Nail a ledge across the front and back 2 ins. from the bottom edge to carry the floor, and cut off sufficient board for it, making it a loose fit so that it may quite readily be taken out and scrubbed.

An exit should be cut about 8 ins. high and 6 ins. wide, and rounded at the top (as dotted in Fig. 86), and a rebated runner should be placed on each side so that a door may be slipped down at night to keep the chicks warm. A piece of wire netting, 1 ft. wide and of 1-in. mesh, should now be fastened with staples securely over the opening in front. The top should be in three pieces. Cut off nine lengths of board 2 ft. long, fasten three lengths together with battens to form the door over the sleeping compartment, three more to form the door at the other end of the run, and the remaining three lengths to be nailed securely in the middle of the top of the shed. Two pairs of hinges will be required at the back of the top doors, so that they can be lifted from the front. The top should be covered with roofing felt in three pieces, the two end pieces overhanging the middle piece about 3 ins. Then, as there is no fastening to the top, it is impossible for cats or dogs to get in.

The chief advantage of this structure is its portability; also it gives the chicks plenty of room to run about. It can also be moved to a fresh spot every day if on grass. If no grass is available, the run can be littered down with 3 ins. or 4 ins. of road sweepings, or anything dry, or even with a good thickness of chopped straw—intensive-house style.

CHAPTER VI

Hurdles, Fences, etc.

HURDLES FOR A FIXED RUN.—When a house is fitted with a run, a good way to make it will be in the form of hurdles, such as those shown in Figs. 87 and 88, any number from four upwards of Fig. 87 being used for the sides, and one of Fig. 88 for the end farthest from the house. The hurdles shown are intended to form a covered run, 2-in. wire netting being used over the top. This may be fastened to the top rail of the hurdles on one side and tied to the other side with wire. If the run is wide the roofing nets should have a wire reeved through the selvedge edges where they join, and should be supported with a prop under the wire in the centre of the run.

If a docile class of fowl is kept, the hurdles may be made 6 ft. high, and it will not be necessary to cover the top of the run with netting. To make one of the hurdles, get out four uprights 5 ft. 2 ins. long by 2 ins. by 2 ins. Next prepare two rails 6 ft. long and of the same size as the uprights. The top rail may be halved to the uprights, and the middle rail halved-tenoned into the outside posts and halved to the middle ones. The joints should be secured with screws or strong nails driven through and clinched (i.e. turned over at their projecting points); holes should be bored for the nails to prevent splitting the wood. The bottom rail consists of a 6-in. by ¾-in. board nailed to the uprights as shown at A (Fig. 87). The upper portion of each hurdle is covered with wire of 2-in. mesh, and the lower with 1-in. mesh, the object of the latter being to prevent small chickens getting through if the run is used for rearing. In fixing the wire, nail the ends and top of the upper piece, and the ends and bottom of the lower piece, allowing about 1 in. between the upper and lower net; do not stretch too tightly lengthways. The two nets can then be drawn together at the joint with a pair of pliers and wired or nailed to the middle rail; this will stretch the nets tightly on the frame. The construction of the end hurdle (Fig. 88) is somewhat similar, with the exception that a 2½-in. or 3-in. rail is used at the bottom, and all the joints, except at the top, are preferably mortised and tenoned. A doorway is shown on one side, and the lower netting on the other replaced with upright bars. A trough for water or soft food may be placed outside this portion. The door may be of 2½-in. or 3-in. by 1¼-in. stuff, except the bottom rail, which should be wider. A brace is fitted in the corners of the lower portion of the door frame, as shown in Fig. 88, to keep it square. A pair of cross-garnet or T hinges may be used for hanging the door, and a hook and staples fitted on the shut side for a padlock. A strip of wood must be nailed on the post against which the door closes, to prevent it falling in beyond the surface of the frame.

Poultry Fences or Movable Runs.—It is unwise to make poultry runs into fixtures, for a change of ground is conducive to health in the stock. Thus hurdles or movable stakes make ideal fences. A convenient size for the hurdles (see Fig. 89) is 6 ft. by 6 ft., irrespective of the portions inserted in the ground. Made of 1½-in. square bars, and covered with wire netting, a hurdle is very strong. The points entering the ground may be between 1 ft. and 2 ft. long; but before the hurdles are brought into use these points should be coated with coal-tar.

Another type of hurdle and gate to correspond is shown by Figs. 95 and 96. It is possible to produce these in quite a substantial manner without joints of any description by simply nailing the parts together as indicated. If desirable, another horizontal rail could be introduced across the centre of the wire netting. It will be noticed that the lower portion is boarded instead of open, thus serving to ward off draughts, more particularly from the very young birds and to prevent fighting. The gate has a long brace, the lower end of which should be on the hinged side.

Stakes to Support Wire Netting.—Movable stakes are very useful where large numbers of poultry are kept, as then runs can be quickly erected and re-moved. One of these stakes is shown in Fig. 90. In the top a **V** is cut, and a piece of thin ribbon-iron, bent as shown in Fig. 91, is then fixed on the head of the post. Another piece of ribbon-iron, bent as shown in Fig. 92, is also attached to the side of the post, at a point which will be level with the surface of the ground when the stake is in use.

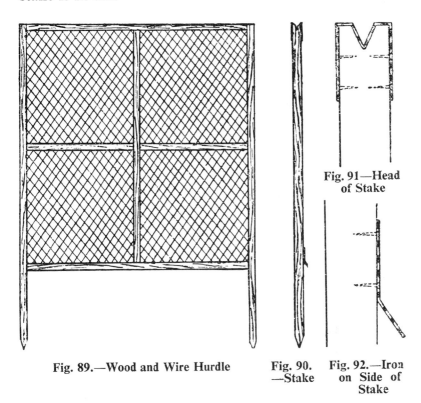

Fig. 91—Head
of Stake

Fig. 89.—Wood and Wire Hurdle   Fig. 90.   Fig. 92.—Iron
                                      —Stake   on Side of
                                                    Stake

To construct a poultry fence, these stakes are fixed in the ground, and the wire netting is hung on them by means of the **V** at the top and the piece of iron in Fig. 92. Thus nails and staples are dispensed with. Of course, these thick wooden stakes are only suitable when wire netting with a large mesh is employed, as, obviously, the head of a 2-in. square post could not be threaded through a ½-in. wire mesh. The length of the stakes naturally depends on the width of the wire netting. The heaviest breeds will not often try to

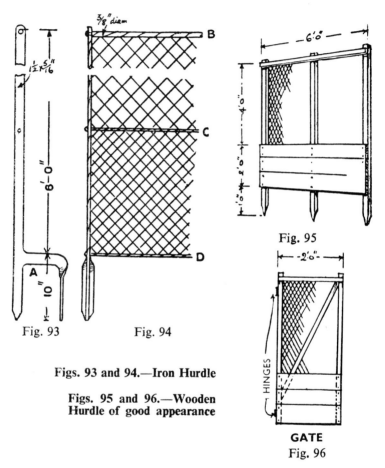

Fig. 95

Fig. 93   Fig. 94

Figs. 93 and 94.—Iron Hurdle

Figs. 95 and 96.—Wooden Hurdle of good appearance

GATE
Fig. 96

clear a 3-ft. 6-in. fence; most heavy breeds will stay behind a 5-ft. fence, but light birds will often clear a much higher hurdle. A 6-ft. fence, however, is the usual and most useful size.

CHAPTER VII

Various Poultry Houses Described in Detail

THIS chapter deals with a representative selection of some of the older designs of houses, presenting novel features, while most of them include various suggestions and details capable of adaptation to other houses at the discretion of the reader. Materials and methods of construction are dealt with in Chapter I.

Lean-to or Slant-roof Houses.—*First Example :* Suitable material required for the fowlhouse shown in Fig. 97 will be unplaned deal battens, 2 ins. by 2 ins., and matchboarding ¾ in. by 6 ins. wide. The front consists of five battens 5 ft. long, halved together so as to form a frame 5 ft. square (see Fig. 98), and fastened firmly with nails or screws. The part marked A (Fig. 98) will form the doorway, the other half B being covered with vertical matchboard as in Fig. 99. From the first plank C cut out a small piece at the top and bottom, so as to allow the two cross planks, each 2 ft. 7 ins., to be fastened to the uprights.

For the sides, make two frames as shown in Fig. 100, using three lengths of battens, 5 ft., and one of 4 ft., for each frame. Fasten firmly together, and

65

cover with the matchboarding. Saw off the portions
of matchboarding overlapping the frames at the top.
From the second and third plank cut out a ventilating
hole 6 ins. square. This should be covered with small-

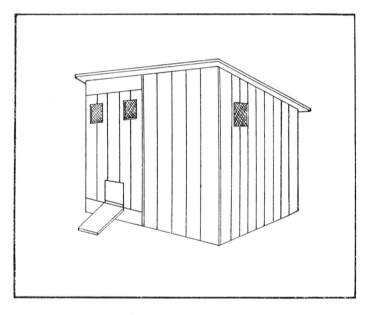

Fig. 97.—Lean-to House

mesh wire netting fastened on the inside (see Fig. 101).
Form the back of two 5-ft. and two 4-ft. battens
halved together. Add a top and bottom rail, each
5 ft. long and halved in position.

Having completed the four sides, screw them together, taking care to use good long and strong screws,

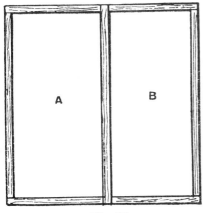

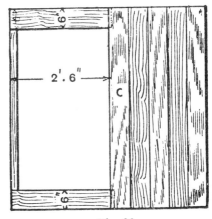

<table>
</table>

A   B

2'. 6" C

Fig. 98   Fig. 99

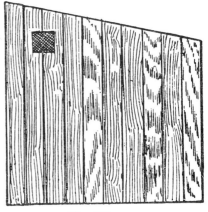

Fig. 100   Fig. 101

Fig. 98. — Front
  Framework
Fig. 99. — Method
  of Matchboarding
Fig. 100. — Side
  Framework
Fig. 101. — Side,
  showing Ventila-
  tor
Fig. 102. — Outside
  of Door

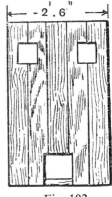

- 2'. 6"

Fig. 102

and then proceed to put on the top. This will consist of eleven planks 5 ft. 6 ins. long, which must be so nailed as to allow 3 ins. to project over each side.

For the door (Fig. 102), fasten together five planks 4 ft. long with battens 2 ft. long on the inside. From the first, second, fourth, and fifth planks cut out near the top a piece 3 ins. wide and 6 ins. deep for windows, the glass being put on the inside and kept in place by means of thin strips of wood. The middle plank need only be 3 ft. long, so as to leave a passage for the fowls as shown. A small door the exact size of the opening allowed must be made, and should be fastened to the large door by a small pair of hinges. To complete the roof, cut ten light strips or fillets 5 ft. 6 ins. long, and nail over the joins in the matchboards.

The material required is as follows: 140 ft. unplaned battens, 2 ins. by 2 ins.; 200 ft. matchboarding, ¾ in. by 6 ins.; lock for door; one pair **T** hinges; one pair small hinges.

Second Example: —A popular size for small poultry houses to-day is 6 ft. by 4 ft., the height being anything between 4 ft. and 7 ft. Necessarily a lofty house gives a purer atmosphere. The general appearance of a lean-to poultry house is shown by Fig. 103. The door and window are in the front, the exit for the fowls is at one end, and a ventilator is placed just underneath the eaves in each end. The interior arrangements are illustrated by Fig. 104, A being the fowls' exit, B the nest-boxes, C the perches (which should be

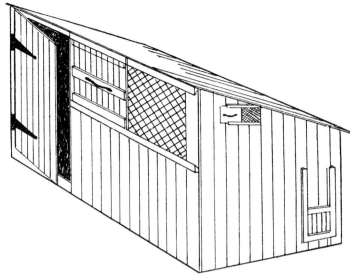

Fig. 103.—Another Lean-to House

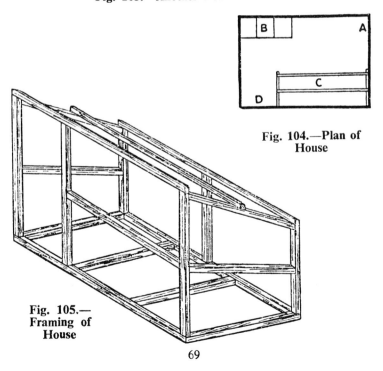

Fig. 104.—Plan of House

Fig. 105.—
Framing of
House

movable, and 1 ft. 6 ins. above the floor), and D the door.

First the frame (see Fig. 105) must be constructed. All the joints are ordinary halvings or mortise-and-tenon joints, with the exception that the middle roof-rail is merely nailed on the rest of the structure. Here it may be mentioned that when nails are largely employed in these and similar structures they should preferably be put in on the slope.

For floors, sides, and roof $\frac{3}{4}$-in. tongued-and-grooved matching will be found suitable. The large and small ventilating shutters run in rebates, the large shutter being useful on hot summer days and nights, when it should be left open to keep the house cool. The small shutters, one in each end, are used when climatic conditions prevent the use of the large one. The shutter which closes the fowls' exit is seen in Fig. 103.

If the building is to be used as a field house or movable house, fix it on strong wrought-iron axles and stout 1-ft. 1-in. wheels, so that it can be pushed into the required position.

Third Example: —Fig. 106 shows an easily constructed house and run which, if built to the sizes given in the following figures, would comfortably accommodate about ten fowls. It can be made with or without a boarded floor, which is, however, always an advantage, and the framework is shown by the dotted lines in Figs. 107 and 108, the latter showing in conjunction with Fig. 110 a very suitable arrangement of the

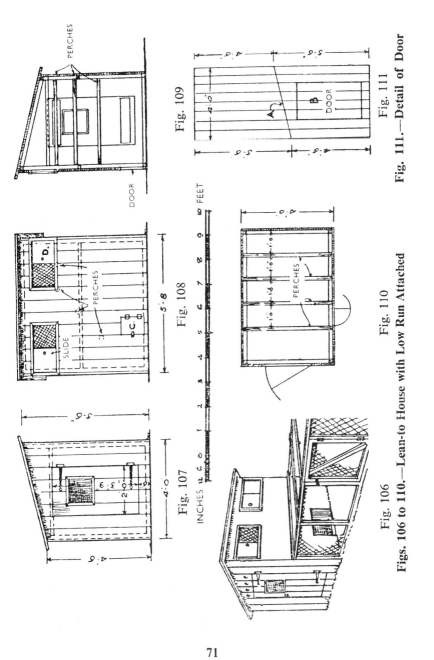

Fig. 109

Fig. 108

Fig. 107

Fig. 111

Fig. 111.—Detail of Door

Fig. 110

Fig. 106

Figs. 106 to 110.—Lean-to House with Low Run Attached

71

perches which could be supported on blocks fixed to the front and back. The boarding of the ends can be obtained without waste by putting a number of 10-ft. lengths together as in Fig. 111, and sawing obliquely across as at A. The door is also cut out as at B, and completed by a couple of ledges across the inside and the insertion of a square of glass as in Figs. 107 and 109. On the front should be arranged a hen-door as at C in Fig. 108, and at the top two ventilating openings at least 12 ins. square, capable of being closed by means of square wood or sheet-iron shutters, sliding in rebated wooden frames as at D. Ventilation is a most important point to consider, and it will be as well to cut some 1 in. diameter holes over the door and along the top of the back to allow for a gradual change of the air even when the large ventilators are closed. Inside or outside nesting-boxes can be used as described on an earlier page, and a run with small gate formed as in Fig. 106, or if more convenient this could be contrived at the side or back. Part of it might be covered in with boarding.

Fourth Example:—This house is similar in general form to the preceding, and unquestionably belongs to a very economical class of structure, and one suitable for extension to any degree by increasing the length without adding to the cost of widening the span beyond 6 ft. or 7 ft., which is, without doubt, the cheapest maximum width.

It will be observed with the design given the

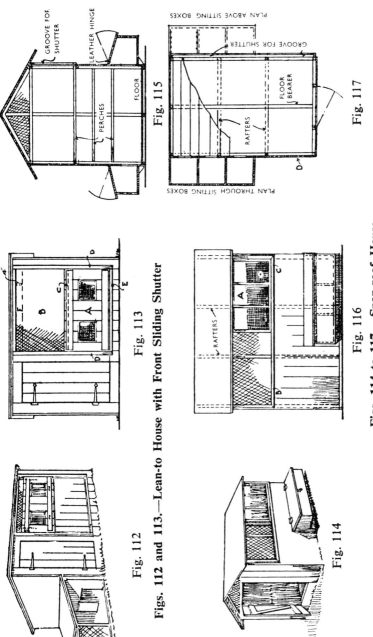

GROOVE FOR SHUTTER

LEATHER HINGE

PERCHES

FLOOR

Fig. 115

PLAN ABOVE SITTING BOXES

GROOVE FOR SHUTTER

RAFTERS

FLOOR BEARER

D

Fig. 117

PLAN THROUGH SITTING BOXES

D

A

B

C

E

E

D

Fig. 113

Figs. 112 and 113.—Lean-to House with Front Sliding Shutter

RAFTERS

A

B

C

Fig. 116

Figs. 114 to 117.—Span-roof House

Fig. 112

Fig. 114

73

attendant's access door is placed on the front, the run being at one side, although these points would be varied according to position and circumstances. The principal new feature incorporated in this house is the sliding shutter at A in Fig. 113, and is shown lowered in Fig. 113 and fully raised in Fig. 112. The house is first built in the ordinary way, leaving a large opening at B, which extends downwards as far as the dotted line C, below which is the ordinary boarded filling (Fig. 112). The opening is covered in with wire netting, perhaps stiffened by a central wooden upright, and a rebated fillet fixed on at either side as at D D to form grooves in which the shutter may slide, a horizontal stop (E) being planted on along the bottom. The shutter itself is ledged up in the usual manner, and should have one or two panes of stout glass inserted in order to light the interior when the shutter is raised in bad weather. It should be made of such a height that when completely raised it leaves a 4-in. opening for ventilation along the top, as at F in Fig. 113, and shown also in Fig. 112. This opening will be sufficiently protected from rain by the overhanging front of the roof, and the shutter can easily be suspended, either in a fully or partially closed position, by means of a couple of hanging cords or chains in conjunction with short hooks. Two bow-handles on the shutter will facilitate its movement. Part of the run might be roofed in as shown, the boarding used being slightly sloped in order to throw off the rain.

Span-roof Houses.—*First Example:* A span or ridge roof is rather more trouble to construct, although at the same time more presentable for isolated positions. Fig. 115 shows it with a boarded floor, which should have a bearer down the centre, as in Fig. 117. This figure also indicates two pairs of rafters which should be fixed over the uprights in the sides. The back is fully boarded, as are also the ends with the exception of the triangular spaces, which are left open for ventilation and protected with wire. The front is boarded rather more than half-way up from the floor on the left-hand half (Fig. 116) and for the full height on the right. The front of the latter is fitted with a three-paned glazed shutter or screen as at A, sliding in grooved guides as at B—C and along the top. The effect of this is, that when necessary the shutter can be pushed along to cover the left-hand half (which is only covered with wire), thus excluding the weather but still admitting plenty of light, while good ventilation without draught is ensured by the open tops of the ends. A shutter sliding horizontally is obviously much less trouble to manipulate than one with a vertical movement, and does not require fixing in any position. On the other hand, of course, it does not distribute the light and sun quite so evenly over the interior.

The door can be at one end, as shown, or at the back (D, Fig. 117), and projecting nest-boxes can be fitted on one or both sides, those under the top openings in Fig. 116 being the best situated, because they

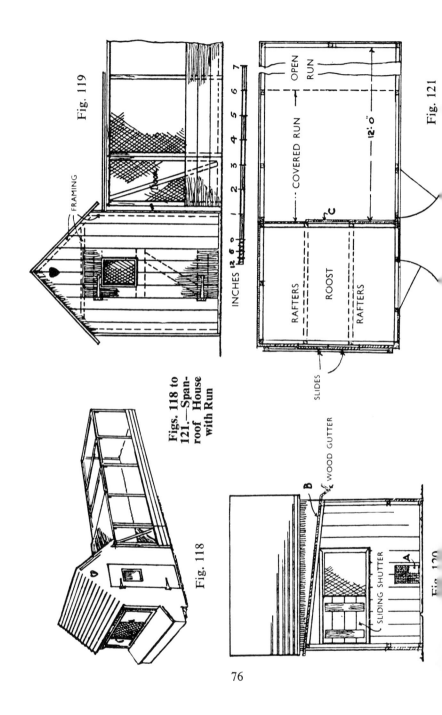

Fig. 119

FRAMING

INCHES 12 6 0 1 2 3 4 5 6 7

Fig. 118

Figs. 118 to 121.—Span-roof House with Run

Fig. 121

OPEN RUN

COVERED RUN

12'.0"

C

RAFTERS

ROOST

RAFTERS

SLIDES

B

WOOD GUTTER

SLIDING SHUTTER

A

Fig. 120

76

are away from the direct light. They are approached internally by means of the usual circular holes, and from without via the sloping tops, which can be hinged with strips of leather. Several perches should be placed transversely across the house. If an enclosed run is necessary it can be arranged on whichever side is most convenient, and a hen-door formed to suit.

Second Example : Fig. 118 shows a workable design, in which the appearance has received consideration with a view to an attractive result. First of all, there is a house for roosting, covered with a steep span roof of weather-boarding, and having a heart-shape pierced in each gable end. The door has a square of glass or netting inserted, while the lower part of the left-hand side is occupied with a range of nest-boxes, above which is a central opening of wire netting, capable of being closed wholly or partially by means of a couple of slides or shutters sliding horizontally in rebated fillets and fitted with bow-handles.

A small door, as at A in Fig. 120, leads from the house to the run, which in all cases where possible should extend to at least 12 ft. in length. About 5 ft. of it next the house may with advantage be roofed in, for use in bad weather, with boarding sloping as at B in Fig. 120, to deliver into a simple wooden gutter at the back; if this is done it will be obvious that no rain from the main roof will be discharged into the run. Assuming this covered part of the run to be provided, the house can be ventilated, even when the outer opening has to be closed, by means of another opening fitted with wire and a sliding shutter, as at c in Fig. 121, and seen also in Fig. 120. The run is shown fairly high, and should have an access door, braced as in Fig. 119; it can be boarded for the 1 ft. 6 in. near ground, in order to give a little shelter to its occupants.

Lean-to House.—Figs. 122 to 126 show a house capable of accommodating at least fifteen adult birds intensively if made to the sizes given. It is particularly adapted to exposed positions. It consists of a roost complete with projecting nest-boxes, connected with a larger scratching shed, beyond which an open run can be arranged. While the roost can advantageously have a boarded floor, the outer compartment should be open to the earth.

The roost has an attendant's door on the front, and also a large glazed window, as at A in Fig. 123, hinged at the top to open outwards and adjusted by means of a casement stay at the bottom. Above the window will be noticed a small wire strip, B, permanently open for ventilation, which is further provided for by means of the panel of wire in the side next the scratching compartment, shown at c in Fig. 124. This figure will best serve to explain the arrangement of the latter compartment, which can have an open outer end if not too exposed, but would otherwise be entirely boarded in on the back and end. Its roof slopes to the back, but finishes in the front with a sloping hood projecting 15 ins. or 18 ins. as at D, and supported on triangular brackets, as seen in Fig. 122.   Beneath this hood and

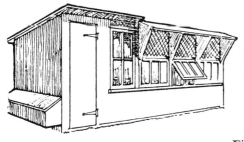

Figs. 122 to 124—Lean-to House, with Hoods, etc.

Fig. 122

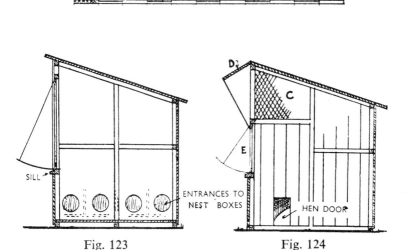

Fig. 123   Fig. 124

sheltered by it are open panels of wire netting, below which is a horizontal rail to which are hinged small glazed lights, as at E in Fig. 124 and F in Fig. 125.

Below these is a projecting piece to serve as a sill, and the remainder of the front is filled in with boarding as indicated. In setting out the work it will look best if the panes of glass to the smaller lights can be made to

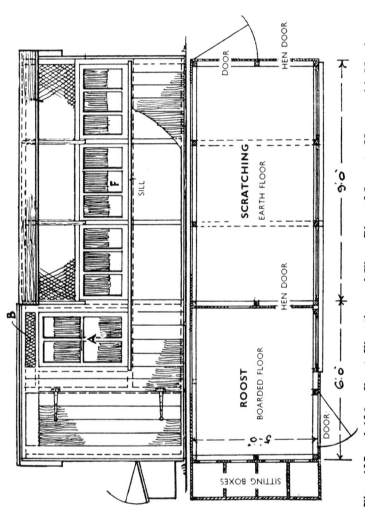

Figs. 125 and 126.—Front Elevation and Floor Plan of Lean-to House, with Hoods, etc.

coincide with the lower ones of the large light to the roost.

Extended Lean-to House.—Fig. 127 shows a type of house suitable for extension by a simple repetition of the parts to any desired length.   One of its bays is shown in section in Fig. 130, where the usual dropping-

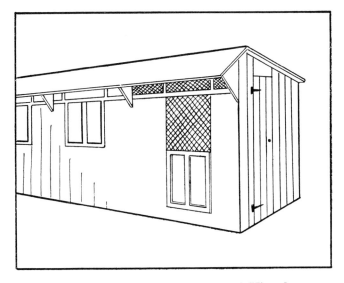

Fig. 127.—House with Hood and Hinged Shutter

board is seen supported on an end-rail A.   The top front has a wooden hood similar to that in the last example, shielding an open space at B (see also C in Fig. 128).   Below this in the centre of the 6-ft. bay is an opening, covered in with wire and capable of being closed when necessary by means of frames filled in with glass or canvas, hinged at the bottom, as at D in

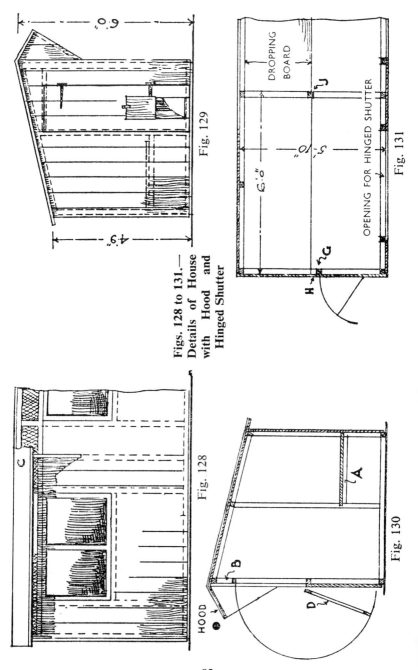

6′.0″

4′.9″

Fig. 129

DROPPING BOARD

6′.0″

5′.10″

OPENING FOR HINGED SHUTTER

J

G

H

Fig. 131

Figs. 128 to 131.—
Details of House
with Hood and
Hinged Shutter

C

Fig. 128

HOOD

B

A

D

Fig. 130

82

Fig. 130. They would be kept in position when closed by means of turn-buckles at the top, and are shown raised and lowered in Fig. 127. Alternatively they could slide up and down in rebated guides.

Doors should be provided in the ends, as in Fig. 129, and can be furnished with small hen-doors at the bottom as shown, closed when necessary by means of a hinged flap. The fronts of the intermediate units of the house will be similar to those of the end portions in every way, unless it be desired to arrange a door in one of them instead of at the ends, which might then be reserved for runs. A long house of this description could be separated into two distinct divisions by means of a central partition, or there are other variations of which it is capable. The upright G (Fig. 131) is decentralized to suit the door, for which it forms a rebate, as it projects a little beyond the boarding at H, whereas the upright J is in the centre of the piece of framing.

Span-roof House with Sheltered Scratching-place.— The house illustrated by Figs. 132 to 137 would accommodate about ten fowls, and differs from the other houses in having a sheltered scratching-place under the roosts.

To make the house, prepare a simple framework on the usual lines as dotted in the figures. Notch and secure each joint with a couple of 2-in. No. 14 wood screws. See that the frame is square, and nail on the boarding. On one side, leave five spaces in the position shown at A (Fig. 133), which may be fitted with doors hinged with a strip of leather at the top and fitted with a button at the bottom, for the purpose of gathering eggs from the nest-boxes. A doorway 12 ins.

Fig. 132.—Span-roof House with Underneath Run

by 8 ins. is cut in the front end in the position shown at B (Fig. 134), and slide pieces are nailed on each side of this to enable the door to be lifted, an iron pin being used to hold it in position, or it may be hung with a pulley and cord. At the top a large opening is cut at each end and filled in with $\frac{3}{4}$-in. mesh wire for the purpose of ventilation, a sliding shutter, as shown at the top of Fig. 134, being used to regulate the amount of air for cold or warm weather if the position be very exposed. The inside of the back end is shown in Fig. 136. A doorway is provided at this end, and the boards are brought down to the ground, but the bottom rail is kept up $3\frac{1}{2}$ ins., so that the notches in the corner-posts for this rail and the side sills do not come opposite each other. The object in keeping the front end 2 ft. above the ground, as shown in Fig. 134, is to provide a dry run for the fowls, and this should have dust-baths or should be covered with a few inches of dry earth and fine ashes. The floor is covered with 1-in. matchboarding supported on two or three joists 4 ft. 4 ins. long by $2\frac{1}{2}$ ins. by 2 ins. to which the boards may be nailed. The floor at the ends rests on the end rails, but should not be nailed if the house is built to take apart.

In fitting up the inside, five fixed nest-boxes are provided. To make these, fillets $1\frac{1}{2}$ ins. by 1 in. are nailed to the inside of the house, to which a shelf 1 ft. 2 ins. above the floor and the full length of the house is fixed. The space under this is divided into compartments, as shown in Fig. 137, an outside door being provided for each at A (Fig. 133), and a strip $2\frac{1}{2}$ ins. wide C (Fig. 136) nailed along the front. Three perches are used, two being across the house and one running lengthwise in the centre. These may be made by sawing a pole $2\frac{1}{2}$ ins. or 3 ins. in diameter

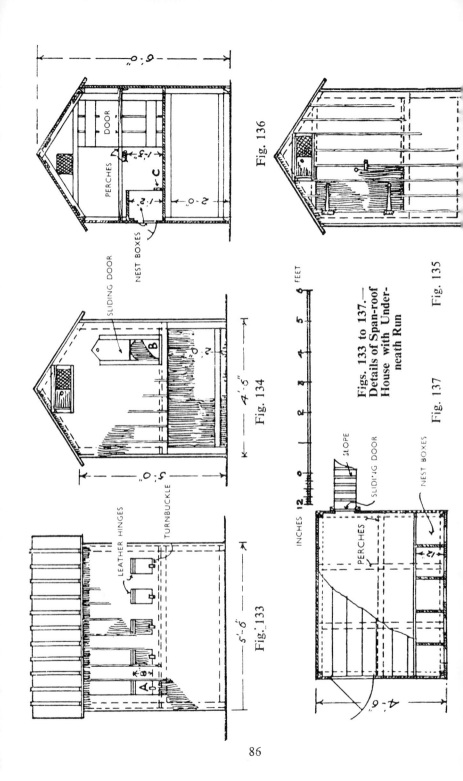

Figs. 133 to 137.—Details of Span-roof House with Underneath Run

Fig. 133

Fig. 134

Fig. 135

Fig. 136

Fig. 137

86

through the centre, the ends resting on fillets nailed to the ends and sides of the house. The top of the perches should not be more than 1 ft. 6 ins. above the floor. A ladder, made by nailing strips across a 7-in. by 1-in. board, must be provided to enable the fowls to enter the house from the run.

A poultry house of this description can be fitted with iron wheels, but if the wheels are only wanted occasionally, wooden ones will serve the purpose. Two pairs of wheels can be used for a large house, and one pair, fixed in the centre, will be sufficient for small houses. The wheels can be fixed to the house only when required for moving, especially if one pair is used. They would then be taken off and stored in a dry place, and by this means one set of wheels will serve for a number of houses.

The axle arms (Fig. 138) may be of four pieces of $1\frac{1}{4}$-in. round iron about 12 ins. long, flattened at one end, with a $\frac{3}{8}$-in. hole drilled at A for a split pin, a $\frac{1}{2}$-in. square hole punched at B, and a $\frac{1}{2}$-in. round hole drilled at C for bolts. The arms are let into two ash beds $2\frac{1}{2}$ ins. square, as shown at A (Fig. 139). One bolt B should project $3\frac{1}{2}$ ins. above the bed to pass through the sill of the house, to which it is secured with a washer and the nut C (Fig. 139). The wheels may be made of elm or any hard wood $2\frac{1}{2}$ ins. thick, sawn or turned to 9 ins. in diameter. Two plates, 3 ins. by $\frac{1}{4}$ in., are screwed across the grain on each side to prevent splitting and to act as bearings for the axles. A washer is used inside and outside the wheel to prevent the plates rubbing on the end of the bed or on the split pin. When the wheels are not in use, they may be taken off by removing the split pin, and the beds may

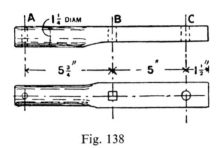

Figs. 138 and 139.—Axle and Wheel of Portable House

Fig. 138

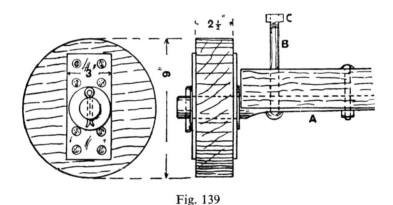

Fig. 139

be left on to act as sleepers for the house, or the bed and wheels may be removed bodily by levering up the ends of the house and taking off the nut c (Fig. 139).

The house as above described would be particularly suitable for an orchard or field, in which it can be frequently moved if it is necessary to confine the fowls to a run, thus giving them the advantage of new ground. Some suggested variations upon it are sketched in Fig. 140, where is shown a house permanently mounted on a stout underframing to form runners, upon which it can be drawn along when

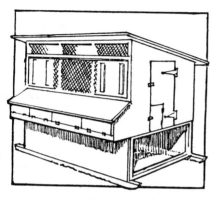

Fig. 140

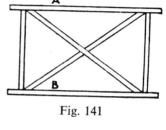

Fig. 141

Figs. 140 and 141.—
Portable House on
Runners

necessary. Without a very strong base such a procedure would strain and rack a house badly, but a sledge constructed as in Fig. 141 and strongly tenoned at the joints would be satisfactory, and the house could be built up on it in the ordinary way. The runners A and B might be 4 ins. by 3 ins. set upright, and the cross-pieces the same, or perhaps 3 ins. by 3 ins. fixed flat, thus leaving an inch clearance next the ground. Rings might be bolted on to facilitate moving.

The house shown in Fig. 140 is on similar lines to that in Fig. 132, but has a simpler roof and projecting

nest-boxes, both of which features are open to altera-
tion. Suitable dimensions for the whole would be 6 ft.
by 4 ft. or 7 ft. by 5 ft. As the boxes are well above
the ground their fronts might be arranged to open
for egg-collection, instead of the sloping tops. Above
them will be seen a large wired opening, capable of
being closed when necessary with two ledged shutters
sliding in grooves as previously described. Above
these, again, and at the extreme top, is an opening
about 7 ins. wide, made permanently open for ventilation well above the heads of the birds. If projecting
boxes are employed the door can be in the centre of
the end, and the drawing will sufficiently explain a
suggestion for incorporating a small door for the birds
with a larger one for the attendant, this arrangement
saving unnecessary cutting of the house. If used in
conjunction with a portable run or enclosure, it may
be advisable to contrive the hen-door at one end and
the larger one at the other. A sloping approach as in
Fig. 132 will, of course, be necessary.

House with Run Underneath.—This is another pat-
tern in which a covered run is provided under the
hen-roost. The house is drawn to the size of 9 ft. by
5 ft., and if built to these dimensions would accommodate comfortably about twenty adult fowls. The
arrangement of the framework will be gathered from
the scale drawings, the plan (Fig. 146) showing the
positions of the uprights as well as of two intermediate
bearers used to stiffen the floor. The boards of the

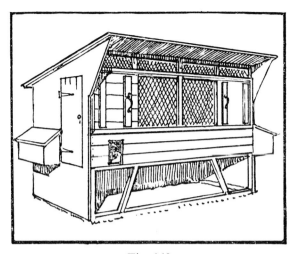

Fig. 142

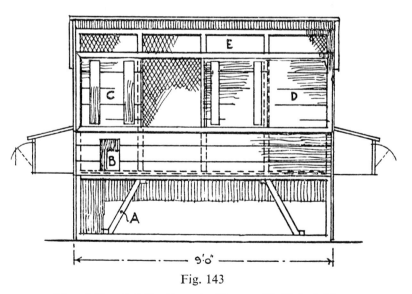

Fig. 143

Figs. 142 and 143.—Lean-to House with Raised Floor

latter run longitudinally. Two sloping struts will be required to stiffen the front rail, as at A in Fig. 143,

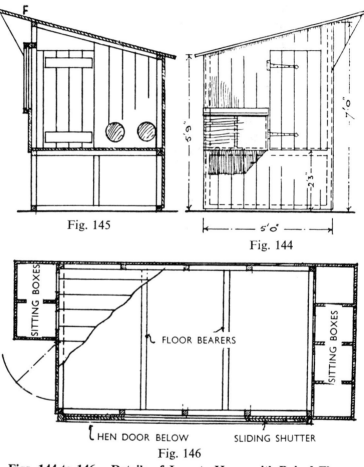

Fig. 145

Fig. 144

Figs. 144 to 146.—Details of Lean-to House with Raised Floor.

and can be framed in position, or secured with small blocks or cleats as shown.

A hen-door with sloping plank is required at B, above which an arrangement of sliding ledged shutters is employed, as in previous cases, whereby the centre of the front can be thrown entirely open or wholly or partially closed at will. At c is the left-hand shutter fully open, and at d the right-hand one completely closed. Above these again, at e, is a narrow continuous ventilating strip, permanently open and sheltered by the projecting boarding of the roof, as at f in Fig. 145, and also by the triangular pieces at the ends, seen in Fig. 142. At one end the necessary door leaves room for only two projecting nest-boxes, but there is just sufficient room for four at the other end.

Ornamental Poultry House.—A picturesque treatment has been aimed at in Figs. 147 to 150, in which the more usual forms of plan have been departed from in order to suit the desired effect of the steep gable-ends having one slope longer than the other. There is nothing special about the framing, which will be readily understood from Figs. 148 and 149. A long roosting-place is entered centrally by means of a plain door, with a diamond-shaped pane inserted (Fig. 147), and should have a dropping-board and perches fixed at either end; opposite the first another door leads to a covered run. These two parts constitute the gabled portion of the work, and should have their roof boarded and well thatched with reed or straw bound strongly down. The roost and a small part of the sheltered run are covered with vertical boarding, but in order to produce the desired effect this should be thick, have square

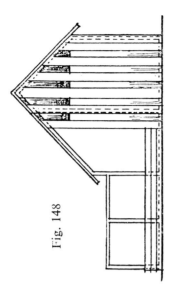

Fig. 148

Figs. 147 to 149.—Artistic Span-roof House

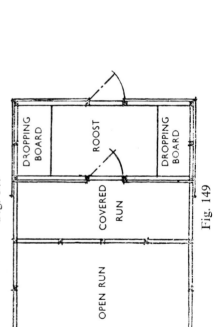

Fig. 150.—Section through Lapped Boarding

Fig. 147

DROPPING BOARD

ROOST

DROPPING BOARD

COVERED RUN

OPEN RUN

Fig. 149

94

edges, and be fixed as in Fig. 150, thus producing a more varied and interesting surface than the usual level faces. It is obviously quite easy to arrange, being merely a matter of setting out on each side.

The ventilating openings in the gables are produced by cutting down the alternate boards, as in Fig. 148, so forming a pleasanter external effect. Either wire netting or wood trellis might be used to fill in the sides of the remainder, as well as of the low open run, except at the bottom, where a few widths of boarding, as in Figs. 147 and 148, are always advantageous. It will be observed that access by the attendant to the covered run is only possible by the inner door from the roost, but a hen-door should be provided between the two compartments.

CHAPTER VIII

Intensive-System Poultry Houses Described in Detail

THE intensive system is one by which the fowls are kept in small or large houses of special design, to which no runs need be attached, the floors being raised well off the ground. Every care is taken to keep the interiors of the houses as dry as possible, and over the floor is spread a good depth of litter: peat moss, chaff, straw, shavings and sawdust for example, or in combination.

First Example: The size given in this chapter (see Figs. 151 to 155) is 18 ft. by 14 ft., 7 ft. high at the front, and 5 ft. at the back, and the house would accommodate approximately sixty birds. Sizes may be varied according to the space available; but it should be remembered that deep houses are preferable to shallow ones. This house has a partition in the centre, shown in Fig. 155, partly boarded and partly covered with wire netting, thus allowing two breeds to be kept separate, that is, two houses in one, each 9 ft. long or wide and 14 ft. deep.

The foundations can be carried out in various ways already described, but the drawings show 4 in. by 3 in. sleepers placed in four rows about 3 ft. 6 ins. apart

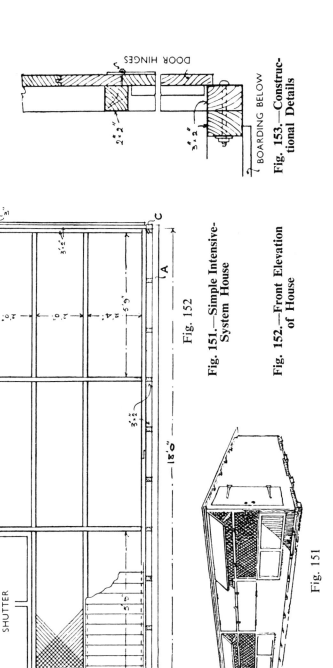

DOOR HINGES

BOARDING BELOW

Fig. 153.—Constructional Details

2" : 2"

3" : 2"

SHUTTER

3' : 2"

3' : 2"

C

A

18' 0"

7' 0"

7' 0"

4' 2"

5' 9"

5' 9"

3"

Fig. 152

Fig. 151.—Simple Intensive-System House

Fig. 152.—Front Elevation of House

Fig. 151

97

either on the ground or layers of bricks, as at A in
Fig. 152 and B in Fig. 154, due care being taken over
the levels.   On the sleepers are placed pieces of scantling, 3 ins. by 2 ins., for the floor joists, one flush with
each end, the remainder at equal distances.

On this base the framework of the four sides can
be erected; it is clearly shown on the figures, each
side being prepared separately and bolted together at
the angles, as in Fig. 153.   Most of the work should
be of about 3-ins. by 2-ins. timber, although some of
the shorter intermediate can be 2 ins. by 2 ins.   It
should be nailed to every floor joist.

The ends are not supported on the joists, but on
two or more pieces nailed to the outside joists, as at
C in Fig. 152, as well as being secured to the front
and back uprights, thus making 4-ins. by 3-ins. corner
posts.

The floor boards can then be nailed in, and a framework similar to the ends fitted to support the rafters
in the centre.   This can be covered with netting to
form a division in the house if required.

The back and ends, also the lowest section of the
front, can now be covered with $\frac{3}{4}$-in. matching, and
the two upper sections of the front covered with wire
netting fixed on the inside.

Framework doors with fine-mesh netting are fixed
inside to allow the wooden doors to be opened in fine
weather for extra ventilation.

At the back of the house, about 2 ft. from the

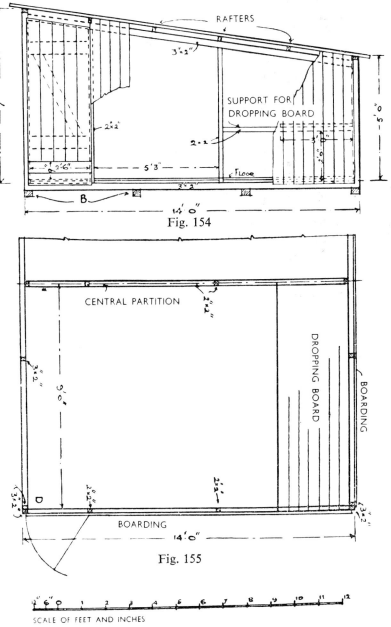

Fig. 154

Fig. 155

SCALE OF FEET AND INCHES

Figs. 154 and 155.—Details of Intensive-system House

99

floor, fix the dropping board (Figs. 154 and 155). This should be 3 ft. wide, and about 6 ins. above this place the perches. The nest-boxes can be placed where desired.

For the six upper divisions of the front make frames of 1½-in. square stuff, to be covered with glass or white calico. The upper three are hinged at the top, and an iron stay secured to fix them open at various angles according to the weather. The lower three can be fastened with buttons, to be taken away in the summer months, or kept fastened in the winter. This house will accommodate sixty birds, thirty in each compartment.

About 550 ft. of 3-ins. by 2-ins. material will be required for the framework, rafters and floor joists; nearly three squares of boards for the roof; just over two and a half squares for the floor; and four squares of matchboarding for outside and dropping boards.

Second Example of Intensive House.—An intensive house of a good average size (namely, 12 ft. by 10 ft.) is explained by Figs. 156 to 160. It would accommodate thirty or so birds. There is nothing special about the general framing, which is fully indicated on the drawings, although attention may perhaps be drawn to the ventilating openings in the sides near the top, and the struts employed to shorten the unsupported span of the rafters, both shown by Fig. 158. This figure also explains the fixed sloping hood along the front, serving to ward off rain and undue heat. For the lower portion the front is covered in with boarding, above which is wire mesh. On each upright of the front framing is fixed a set of pieces

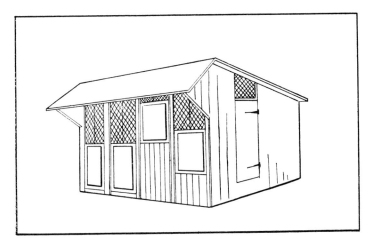

Fig. 156.—12-ft. House on Intensive System

of wood, as shown in section by Fig. 159, two about $2\frac{1}{2}$ ins. by 1 in. and a middle strip about $1\frac{1}{2}$ ins. by $1\frac{1}{4}$ ins., the whole forming a couple of grooves running nearly from top to bottom of the front. In these grooves slide light frames filled in with glass, or linen tightly stretched across.

The frames are stopped at the bottom by small blocks, as at A in Fig. 157, and should just reach from these up to the top of the boarded part of the front, fitting the grooves loosely. They can easily be raised to any desired extent by means of hooks and light

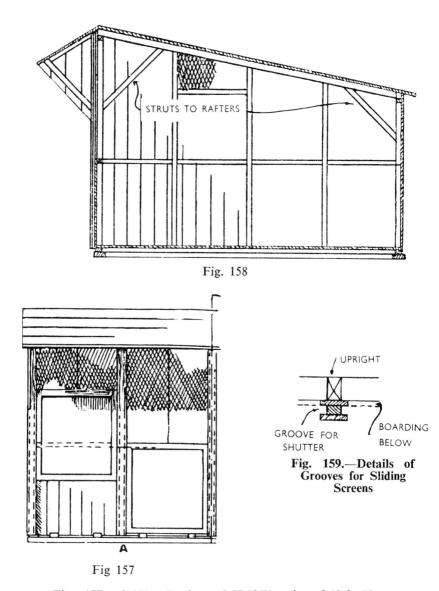

STRUTS TO RAFTERS

Fig. 158

UPRIGHT

GROOVE FOR
SHUTTER

BOARDING
BELOW

Fig. 159.—Details of
Grooves for Sliding
Screens

A

Fig 157

**Figs. 157 and 158.—Section and Half-Elevation of 12-ft. House
on Intensive System**

chains, but it will be noted that even when fully raised they still leave a portion of the wired front open, thus ensuring adequate ventilation without risk of draughts or the entrance of rain. The roof-boarding should overhang sufficiently to shelter the top ventilators at the sides.

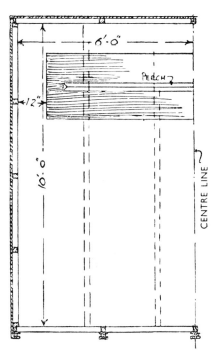

Fig. 160.—Half-plan of 12-ft. House

With regard to the interior, the floor is shown boarded, this being very desirable with intensive houses, as dryness is an essential point. The door is kept well above the floor in order to clear the layer of litter. The perches should be about 1 ft. 6 ins. above the litter, along the back of the house. Nest-boxes can be at the end opposite the door.

Third Example of Intensive House.—As shown in Figs. 161 to 164, this is a comparatively small house (10 ft. by 7 ft.), accommodating perhaps sixteen birds. It is suitable for adaptation to any size: a squarer form is better for units destined for the intensive

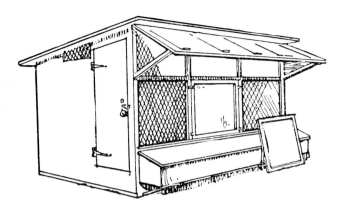

Fig. 161.—10-ft. House on Intensive System

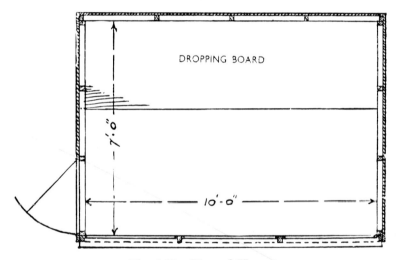

DROPPING BOARD

7'.0"

10'.0"

Fig. 162.—Plan of House

SCALE OF FEET AND INCHES

Scale for Figs. 162 to 164

104

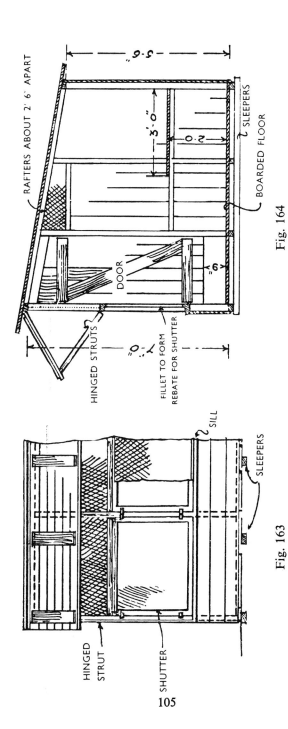

RAFTERS ABOUT 2' 6" APART

5'-6"

3'-0"

2'-0"

SLEEPERS

BOARDED FLOOR

DOOR

6"

HINGED STRUTS

7'-0"

FILLET TO FORM
REBATE FOR SHUTTER

Fig. 164

HINGED
STRUT

SHUTTER

SILL

SLEEPERS

Fig. 163

Figs. 163 and 164.—Half-Elevation of and Cross Section through 10-ft. Intensive House system. Thus 6 ft. by 5 ft., 8 ft. by 6 ft., 10 ft. by 7 ft., 12 ft. by 10 ft., 16 ft. by 12 ft., or 20 ft. by 14 ft. are all suitable proportions of length to width.

The design can be built with or without projecting nest-boxes (shown only in Fig. 161). As before, the bottom of the front is boarded, but higher up there is a horizontal rail dividing the front into upper and lower panels of wire mesh, which should be fixed on the inside. When necessary, the top row of panels can be closed by letting down the sloping hood, which is strongly hinged at the top and supported in its raised position by a couple of stout struts (Fig. 164), hinged to the corner posts of the house. Slots can easily be contrived for their free ends on the under side of the hood, so that it will not be allowed to slip down, and the hood itself can be made up of light boarding held together with cross ledges at intervals. It is just the right width to cover the top panels when the struts are let down. The lower panels of the front require light frames, covered with linen and fitting between the posts and rails. When these are required they can be kept in place with wooden buttons or turn buckles, as indicated on the drawings.

Semi-intensive System.—Under the *semi-intensive system* the layers are allowed out into grass enclosures in good weather, and kept in their house when the conditions are unfavourable, as in the winter months. The same types of intensive laying houses will do for accommodation.

CHAPTER IX

Principles in Poultry House Construction

THE particular design of poultry house chosen will often dictate the positioning of the internal fittings, also the system of ventilation. In all types of houses, arrangements should be made to enable each unit to suit the cold weather of the winter and the extreme heat of the summer.

Light Interiors.—Dark, dismal houses will not mean healthy stock. Glass windows or panels will let in the light. Beneath the droppings-board, in the back of the house, a small wire-netted aperture controlled by a glass slide, lets in light and fresh air, acting as an inlet. It throws light on the litter, and keeps the air cool in hot weather at floor level, also drying the floor-litter. Similar movable glass panels can be placed, low down, in the front of the house.

In a span-roofed structure, drop-in glass windows near the ridge at each end let in light and ventilate the house. In the span roof, too, glass lights every 8 ft. or so would be adopted for a battery laying house, the set on one side being staggered with that on the other.

Fixed glass windows or panels in front or back of the house make the interior too warm, and keep out

direct sunlight, which must penetrate wire-netted apertures, to prevent rickets in chicks and shell-less eggs
in layers.

Inlets and Outlets.—Baffled inlets are best, at lowest
points. The exit, or pop-hole, is often the inlet in a
small house, so place it beneath the droppings-board
which runs along the back. Box ventilators are
baffled inlets, suitable at floor level for incubator
rooms, battery houses, etc. On the outside near floor
level fix a perforated zinc-covered aperture; inside the
house fix against it a shallow box, open only at ends,
and even these can be controlled by slides. Inlets in
the back above the perches mean draughts, unless
beneath the holes thin plywood or the like is fitted,
to form a protective chute.

Outlets in lean-to units are best at highest part of
front, in the form of wire-netting, controlled. Slide-
up glass windows, suspended on a chain from the top,
to be positioned at any desired height, are excellent.
Such windows usually cover the top half of the front
which is wire-netted; a hood at the very top keeps
out the rain. A hinged drop-down shutter, covered
with coarse canvas, is sometimes fitted inside the
house, over any open netting at the top.

In span-roofed buildings, extractor ventilators are
popular fitments at ridge at distances of about 8 ft.
according to size. These are usual outlets in large
brooder, battery and intensive laying houses.

Inner wire-netted doors let in fresh air and direct

sunlight, when the normal door is thrown open, or slides along. Hinged panels, to open, can be made in any solid door.

Droppings-board and Perches.—Droppings-boards are best removable for cleaning, and made to button back when raised for cleaning out floor litter. Usual width is 2 ft. 6 ins. for single length of perch, and approximately 20 ins. off litter; allowances of 1 ft. between perches, and 1 ft. behind and in front of perch. Perch is usually 2 ins. by 2 ins., with slightly rounded top edges, each end fitting in a socket for easy removal for cleaning; about 6 ins. off the droppings-board.

Slatted frames are sometimes used, of 1 in. square slats placed an inch apart, raised on bottom battens several inches off the board.

Perches usually run from end to end of house, but often are fixed at right angles to the back of the house. Linoleum, placed on the board, facilitates clearance of droppings each morning.

The droppings-board is often on the slope, and metal lined, so that the droppings are removed from the back of the house, through a hinged door or flap. The space over the pit is covered with netting of 2 in. mesh. In the hen-yard system, corrugated iron sheets are placed at the front and ends of corner supports, netting is fitted over the top, and the perches arranged some inches above to form a manure pit. Perches may be slightly on the slant, one above the other.

A hinge, to open flap at the back of the house,

would enable the droppings-board to slide out for cleaning, without entering the house.

Portable Units.—Many portable units have slatted floors, which take out in sections, the droppings passing through to a wooden droppings-floor which also slides out at the end. The latter is several inches beneath the slats with space for droppings and fresh air between. One sees this arrangement in night-arks, slatted-floor laying houses, etc. Of span-roof design, such units have ridge ventilation, and the night-ark has a lid in the roof, also a dual sliding door in the front, one of wood and the other of netting for warm nights. Additional ventilation holes may be made in the ends near the ridge. The ridge-cap ventilator also can be lowered and raised.

In the fold pen, at one end where the fowls roost, a slatted or wire floor is fitted, with or without underneath droppings-board. The latter is dispensed with if the fold is moved daily to fresh land to manure it evenly. The rest of the fold is floor-less, for the birds to be on the grass. The sides are low, to give a steep span roof, as protection against cattle, hinged doors being fitted in the roof of run, part of which at one end may be covered in against the weather. Water buckets are suspended inside, and mash containers are pivoted to turn outwards for filling, along the sides and end.

Portable units are moved daily to fresh sites in many cases. Wheels, skids, tow rails, and the like are fitted, also handles.   There are gadgets to move them readily, the same accessory fitting a number of units in turn.

Variety of Nests.—Indoor nest-boxes are often made in sets, provided with legs, in order not to waste the littered floor for the fowls.   There is a wide fly-up board (often slatted) at the base of the nest-fronts, to which the birds fly before entering the compartments to lay.   Such platforms are hinged if desired, so that they close up the fronts, being then buttoned, to keep broodies out of the nests at night, or before pullets start to lay.   The lid is made on the slant, of boarding, to prevent roosting thereon, and a door in this enables one to put the eggs as collected on clean nesting material, to await the day's final collection.

Sets of such nests fit along a partition, or against one end of a large house, or may run the length of the house, against the woodwork of the front, beneath the wire-netted top half, which is controlled by the glass windows.   That makes a secluded spot.   Often the alighting board is the droppings-board, from which the birds fly up to the nest-board to lay, and two tiers are then possible.   Made in sets, they are easily taken out for cleaning.

Outside nest-boxes are fitted in one end, or along the front, depending on the design of the latter.   An excellent design of front is a solid half or so at the bottom, and slide-up, or hinged to drop down, glass windows controlling the top wire-netted part.   Outside nest-boxes get in the way of such windows, and indoor types are better, unless the windows are of the drop-in type, to be taken out in warm weather. The same hinged fly-up is arranged for outside nest-boxes; to keep the interiors of these cool, a piece of asbestos sheeting is fitted above the tops, with air-space between.

Where one desires to record the layers, trap-nest fronts are fitted to the openings of the nests. A trap-front may measure about 12 ins. wide, and slightly more in depth; it is hinged to one upright, and buttoned to the other for easy handling of the layer and cleaning purposes. The sides of the front are grooved, so that a metal or wooden slide will go up and down, and even take out, if the nest is not in use for trap-nesting. When set, a space is left beneath the slide, through which opening the layer enters the nesting compartment to lay. As it goes through it raises the slide with its back, and releases the gadget holding up the slide, which then drops right down, shutting the bird in. When it has laid, and the egg collected has been marked to the leg-ring of the bird, the latter is released, and the front reset. The slide may rest in position on a bent wire, which the layer moves when entering the nest. A simple gadget is to attach a short piece of stout wire, with bent end, around a screw in the side support of nest; fit a screw also in the slide, and place the bent part of wire around it. As the bird lifts the slide, the bent wire will drop down and work the slide.

Community nest-boxes are sometimes used. The entire front is boarded in, but a circular entrance aperture is made in the middle so that the interior is darkened. The front can be hinged or buttoned in. The idea is to discourage egg-eating, and types of community nests are seen in deep-litter houses and in sheds used in conjunction with straw hen-yards.

Broody-coop Attachments.—Broody coops are often attached to the outside wall of the house. One can arrange a hinged flap on the inside of large laying-houses, and thus put broodies from nest to coop without going outside the house.

In fold units the broody coop is often fitted in the apex of the unit.

Food and Water Containers.—Outside water-boxes keep the litter dry. A nest-box arrangement is fitted to the outside of the unit, and inside the house an aperture is cut, being covered with a grid of slats, for the fowls to put their heads through the spaces to get at the water-container in the box. The floor of the latter can be on the slant, with holes in to let water drain outside. It can be a deep box, with grid well inside.

For young stock the water container is placed on a wire-topped frame, beneath which is a receptacle to catch any water that is upset. At each end is a wire-netted run-up. It keeps litter out of the water or food.

In a large house, a slatted topped table is often

used, with an aperture in the centre to take a bucket of water. The trough for the mash, whether wet or dry, can be on legs, off the litter, with a fly-up perch along each side. In deep-litter houses, the fowls may perch along this, where no droppings-board and perch fitment are provided.

One needs to avoid waste in all mash containers, and keep the fowls out of the food. A grid can be placed over the top of the mash trough, to accomplish this. A lip all round the food container will prevent the fowls from pecking out the mash. The handle of a small food-trough is made to spin round to keep the fowls from perching on it.

Where it is desired to control the dry mash, a lid should be fitted. In an open container, the back can be higher than the front, with a slat fixed across the bottom and top of the open part, leaving a space for feeding. Hinged to the top slat provide a lid for closing up container. A diamond-shaped box with open top makes a good non-waste mash container, each end fitted in a strong board support. Provide floor mash troughs with good end supports so that they will not get upset.

It saves labour if water, grit and mash containers can be replenished from outside the unit. Inside grids make this possible.

Automatic food containers are readily made by the aid of an alarm clock, to which there is a connecting link between clock-handle and lid of container. The fowls can thus get their food when the owner is at work, the clock being set for a given time.

Wooden mash-boxes are simple to make, generally 1 ft. or 2 ft. long, the sides about 4 ins. high, the ends 8 ins., with width of 4 to 6 ins. Across the tops of the two ends fit a swinging batten, even a nail driven into each end, fitted beneath staples. The ends can be narrowed towards the tops.

Conversions and Substitutes.—On the farms, one sees in the hen-yard system a method of utilizing disused outbuildings. The selected building is fitted out as a roost, often with manure pit and community nest-boxes, lighting fitted for night feeding, and with proper ventilating arrangements. To this roost is arranged an outside yard, deeply bedded down with straw, which is added to continuously: it is a wired-in enclosure. The floor of the roost is deeply littered, and the interior is made light by suitable conversions in regard to windows, ridge cowls, roof lights, inlets, etc.

Some convert outbuildings as deep-litter houses. Again there must be practical adjustments and alterations in regard to light, ventilation, etc. A dry floor is prepared, cemented down, and litter built up thereon throughout the season. Perching may be along the sides of the dry-mash troughs, which are on legs off the litter. Community nests are provided.

Asbestos sheeting makes an ideal droppings-board, and table units covered with it, the perches fitting

into metal stands.   Where asbestos sheeting is used
in the construction of houses, there must be ample
ventilation to prevent condensation and to keep the
litter dry.

Felt over netted framework can be used to good
effect, particularly in covering runs and small pens.
Main uprights will be of 2 ins. by $1\frac{1}{2}$ ins. battens, and
other framework 2 ins. by 1 in. battens.   The latter
will support felt on the roof if placed at 3 ft. spaces.

Frames covered with wire-netting, then stuffed with
leaves, rushes, straw, or brushwood, will make
shelters, windbreaks, etc.

One can so plan units to have slatted or solid floors.
When the slats are in use, the boarded floor drops
beneath them to act as a droppings-board; when the
solid floor is in use, littered down, the slatted one
goes out of the way beneath it.

Greenfood Rack.—Some use string or wire bags
to contain green food.   One can make a wall rack in
the form of a wire-netted frame, hinged at the bottom, with the top open, like a pocket.   The birds
pull the green stuff through the taut netting.   Roots
can also be placed in such racks.

CHAPTER X

Heated Outdoor Brooders or Chick-Rearers

WHILE the " direct " and " hot-air " methods of heating rearers require less expensive and carefully adjusted fittings, there is no doubt that the hot-water system, properly installed, provides the added advantage that, if by accident or negligence the lamp should go out at any time, the water would maintain practically the same temperature for a considerable period.

Small outdoor brooders or chick-rearers are sometimes made in the form of a heated chamber only. It will be obvious that at times the difference in temperature experienced in passing from the rearer into the outer air must be considerable and likely to do great injury to the fragile chicks. To avoid such risks, with their inevitable disappointments and loss, at least one intermediate stage of temperature should be provided. The enclosed outer compartment, sharing a proportion of the heat, forms a suitable transition to the run, sheltered but open on the sunny side, and it is quite possible to add these to a single-chamber rearer.

A heating system of a very simple nature, suitable for, say, about thirty chicks, is explained by the plan and elevation in Fig. 165. For this size, the tank shown should be about 16 ins. square and $2\frac{1}{2}$ ins. deep, made without the central opening, access being available from the side only of the heated chamber. A 1½-in. flue A rises from the lamp, and passing through the water-tank as dotted on the plan, has an

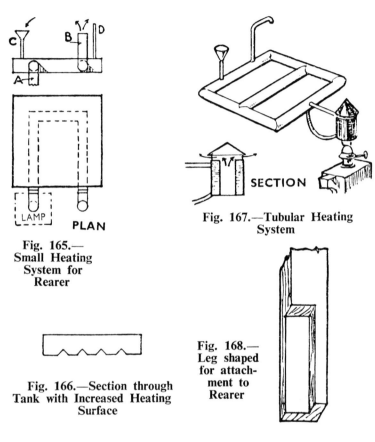

PLAN

Fig. 165.—
Small Heating
System for
Rearer

Fig. 167.—Tubular Heating
System

SECTION

Fig. 166.—Section through
Tank with Increased Heating
Surface

Fig. 168.—
Leg shaped
for attach-
ment to
Rearer

outlet as at B. Both the junctions at A and B should be socketed for removal in order to facilitate cleaning occasionally—a most necessary precaution—and the tank should have a fixed funnel for filling as at C, to-gether with an air outlet D. As the whole value of a tank lies in the amount of heating surface it presents; a corrugated or serrated form is sometimes adopted for the under-side, such as that shown in section by Fig. 166.

In cases where a smaller amount of water at a higher temperature is relied upon for heating, a series of copper pipes about 2 ins. in diameter, arranged as in Fig. 167, can be employed. These have a funnel and air outlet, and the circulation of water through them can be effected by means of a small sheet-iron " jacket-boiler " connected to the pipes by means of $\frac{1}{2}$-in. copper flow and return tubes. Fig. 167 shows a cylindrical boiler with the central space open at the top, but with a flat conical hood or deflector fixed on small wire supports.

Rearers will be found much easier to tend and regulate when it is possible to have them at a convenient level to obviate stooping, this also avoiding the pernicious effects of ground-damp. Some appliances are best lifted on tables or trestles; others can be fitted permanently with legs from the first. When it is desired to add legs, these may suitably take the form shown by Fig. 168, overlapping the sides at least 6 ins., and preferably screwed in order to be easily removed if necessary without undue damage to the other work.

With regard to the capacities of the rearers described in this chapter, some would regard them of 100-chick capacity, but the reader would be wise to limit the number of chicks to about sixty, always avoiding any overcrowding.

Hot-water Rearer.—For the first few weeks of their lives chicken require a well-warmed retreat free from draughts but affording them opportunities for exercise as they gradually develop and become fledged. Such a home, capable of accommodating about sixty inmates, is shown by Fig. 169.

The rearer itself is mounted on legs at a distance of 8 ins. above the ground, this being an important point. It is quite separate from the run, to which it can be attached by means of strong eyes and hooks in the day time, in a sheltered sunny position. At night it can be detached and taken indoors, transit being rendered easy by means of the handles fixed on each side.

In making the rearer the sizes of wood employed can be varied to suit whatever is available; but the work has been set out to suit ordinary light battens and 6-in. by ¾-in. boarding, the tongued-and-grooved variety being desirable, in order to avoid opened joints and the resultant draughts. The whole should be thoroughly painted or coated with preservative externally, while lime-whiting is a suitable internal treatment. The tops can be either exposed wood or covered with good tarred felt.

The run is illustrated by Figs. 169 to 173. The front consists of a framework of 2-in. by 1-in. stuff halved together and filled in with fine wire mesh, the whole measuring 6 ft. 9 ins. by 1 ft. 6 ins. The back consists of two 6-in. boards on small upright battens;

it is joined to the front by end-boards as in Fig. 170, and also by roof-boards as at A in Fig. 172, fixed in position. Between these latter the roof is made in

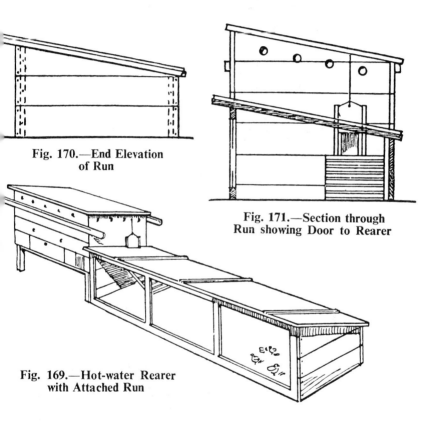

Fig. 170.—End Elevation
of Run

Fig. 171.—Section through
Run showing Door to Rearer

Fig. 169.—Hot-water Rearer
with Attached Run

two sections to lift off, the openings being covered with small fillets as shown. The roof should project a little at the back end, and at least 4 ins. in the front.

The rearer measures 3 ft. 3 ins. by 2 ft. 10 ins., and can easily be built up of external boarding as at B

(Fig. 173), secured to four legs about 2 ins. by $1\frac{1}{2}$ ins. as shown, a floor being added afterwards and notched as necessary to fit round the legs. At the front the rearer is 2 ft. high measuring from the top of the floor (which is about 9 ins. above the ground), and it slopes down to 1 ft. 6 ins. at the back. The top cover can be either hinged or arranged to lift right off, and should overhang a little on all sides, any necessary rails to hold the boarding of it together being arranged on the underside. Handles, projecting 8 ins. and rounded at their ends, are screwed on the front and back.

The internal fittings must, of course, be worked in conjunction with the tank and lamp described later; but generally speaking are as follows: A partition as at c (Figs. 173 and 175), of the full height and width and 6 ins. from the right-hand side, leaving a narrow lamp-compartment. An internal lining round a chamber 2 ft. 4 ins. square (see D), $\frac{1}{2}$ in. thick and 1 ft. 2 ins. high. This leaves a cavity of about 2 ins., through which there is required a cleaning door E (Fig. 172) 1 ft. 7 ins. wide, hinged at the bottom, and contrived so as to fit tightly without draughts. A door as at F, 5 ins. by 6 ins., will also be required for access to the lamp. The cavity and the cleaning-door should be separated at the sides and top by means of strips as at G (Fig. 173). An entrance as at H should also be boxed in as indicated; it is the chicks' approach to the run, and should have a sloping board fitted with small fillets to give a foothold, leading to ground-level.

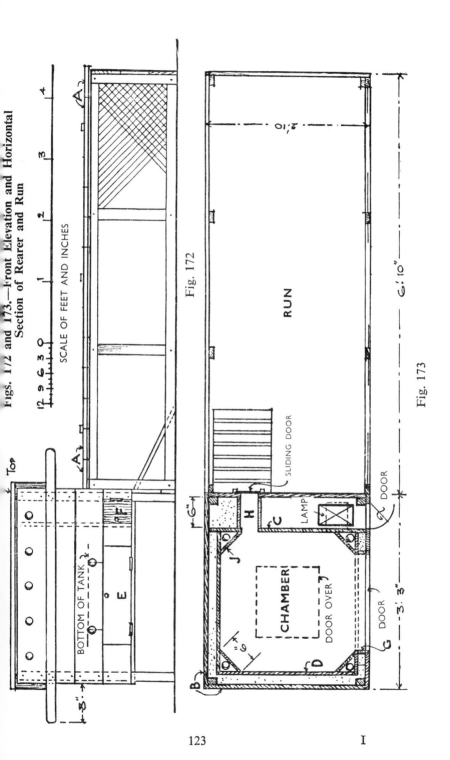

Figs. 172 and 173.—Front Elevation and Horizontal Section of Rearer and Run

SCALE OF FEET AND INCHES

12 9 6 3 0 1 2 3 4

Fig. 172

Fig. 173

TOP

BOTTOM OF TANK

E

3"

RUN

2' 10"

6' 10"

SLIDING DOOR

DOOR

LAMP

CHAMBER

DOOR OVER

6"

H

C

J

D

B

G

G

DOOR

3' 3"

6"

The entrance should have a door sliding in grooved fillets and capable of being fastened open by means of a cord as in Fig. 171. Across each corner of the chamber there is fitted an upright as at J (Fig. 173), 6 ins. wide and 9 ins. high. In each case this has a $\frac{1}{2}$-in. hole taken out of it with a brace and bit $5\frac{1}{2}$ ins. above the floor, this, with a rather larger hole in the floor behind the upright (Fig. 173), serving to introduce fresh air well above the heads of the chicks when the rearer is closed at night. Two outlets for vitiated air are provided as high as possible above the cleaning door (see Fig. 172).

The tank is similar to the type employed in most incubators, and its size and arrangement may be gathered from Fig. 178, which shows it without its fixed top cover. Some readers will doubtless undertake its construction themselves, while others can easily get this portion of the work done for them. It may be of stout zinc, say No. 11 or 12 s.w.g., although sheet-copper would be better, and the flue should in any case be of copper. The tank is boxed up and well soldered together to the overall sizes given, including the $5\frac{1}{2}$-in. by 4-in. projection near the front of Fig. 178; but in the centre there is an aperture K 1 ft. 2 ins. square, the purpose and treatment of which are explained later. The flue is of 2 ins. diameter and about 2 ins. from the sides of the central aperture. It comes up from the lamp (Fig. 175) as at L in Fig. 178, is taken horizontally round three sides of the tank,

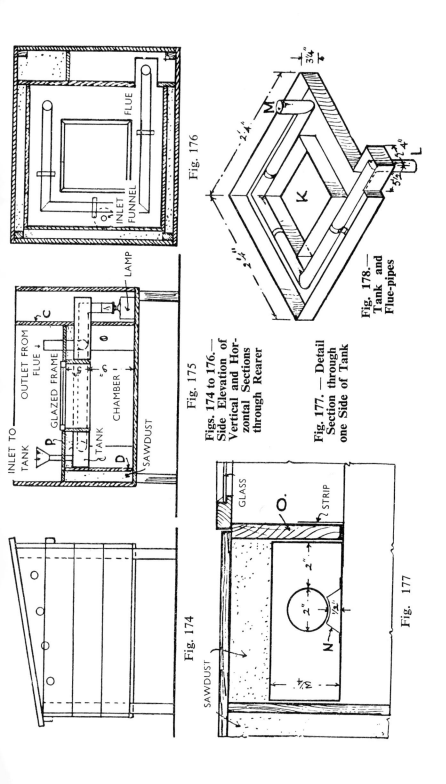

FLUE

Fig. 176

INLET FUNNEL

O

LAMP

OUTLET FROM FLUE

C

GLAZED FRAME

P

3½"

5"

TANK

O

CHAMBER

D

SAWDUST

INLET TO TANK

Fig. 175

Figs. 174 to 176.— Side Elevation of Vertical and Horizontal Sections through Rearer

¾"

M

2'4"

K

2'4"

2"

L

5½"

Fig. 178.— Tank and Flue-pipes

Fig. 177.— Detail Section through one Side of Tank

Fig. 174

SAWDUST

GLASS

O

STRIP

2"

2"

N

½"

3½"

SAWDUST

Fig. 177

mitreing upwards to form an outlet for the fumes as at M (see also Fig. 178). Its ends must be accurately fitted through the top and bottom of the tank, and it can be supported at, say, three intermediate points by means of $\frac{3}{4}$-in. strips bent and soldered on as at N in Fig. 177. An inlet for filling the tank, preferably fitted with a funnel as in Fig. 175, is necessarily flush with the top.

The lamp should consist of a good quality 1-in. burner, mounted on a specially made sheet-tin oil-container about $2\frac{1}{2}$ ins. high, 4 ins. wide, and of any desired length, the burner being planned to come centrally under the commencement of the flue, to which it should be connected by means of a mica chimney or a metal one fitted with a mica inspection piece. A few air inlets should be bored in the floor of the lamp chamber.

In working the rearer, the tank is supported on the sloping pieces across the corners of the chamber (which incidentally obviate the risk of chicks being squeezed into the corners with fatal results); the lamp, when connected up with the flue, raises the water in the tank to a gentle heat, which strikes downwards to the chamber while the fumes escape in the upper part of the rearer, which is accordingly ventilated with holes as in Figs. 171 and 172. First, however, the central aperture in the tank requires lining with 5-in. by $\frac{3}{4}$-in. pieces, as at O in Fig. 177, held by strips soldered to the tank, and bent as shown. These pieces support a glazed frame seen complete in Fig. 175, removable but fitting closely, and provided both for inspection and

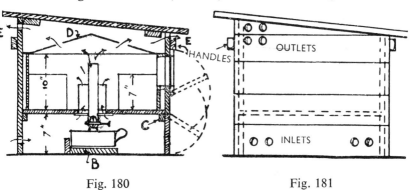

Fig. 179

Fig. 179.—Rearer (and Run) with Direct Heating

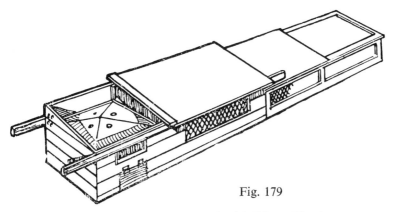

Fig. 180

Fig. 181

Figs. 180 and 181.—Section and End Elevation of Rearer

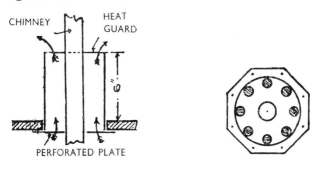

Fig. 182

Fig. 183

Figs. 182 and 183.—Plan and Section of Heat-guard, etc.

127

access purposes. Finally, all the spaces are packed with sawdust to retain the warmth, and boxed in with thin wood as at P (Fig. 175).

A little experimenting and adjustment may be required in connection with the temperature, which should be carefully regulated by means of a thermometer placed near the bottom of the chamber, where it would always tend to be cooler, owing to the tendency of hot air to rise. For the first week a temperature of 90° F. is requisite, reducing approximately by 10° for each of the three following weeks; but in warm weather temperatures might be a trifle lower.

" **Direct-heated** " **Rearer.**—This rearer (see Figs. 179 to 187) comprises a sleeping compartment, heated by a central lamp placed below it as in Fig. 180, and an outer compartment with its floor a few inches lower, but still well above the ground. In fine weather and when the chicks are sufficiently developed, a simple run, such as that shown in Fig. 179, should be attached in order that they may have access to grass. This run might have removable boarded covers with wire guards below them, and if desired there could also be a wire bottom. Alternatively part of the run could be wired over and the remainder boarded.

Handles are shown for easy transit, and a glass or canvas screen should be made to fit over the wire front of the outer compartment when required.

The lamp compartment is about 7 ins. high, and has a ledge and stop across it as at A in Fig. 187 and

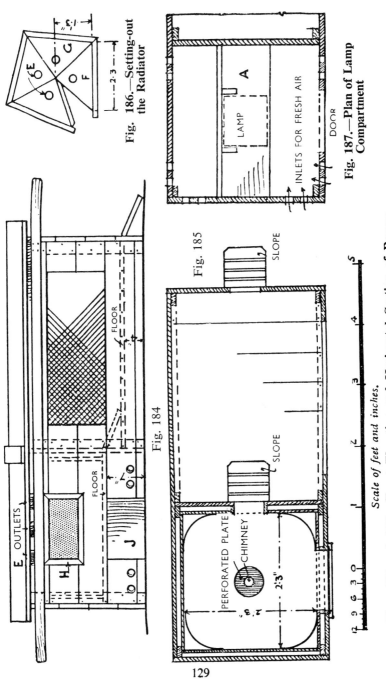

Fig. 186.—Setting-out the Radiator

Fig. 187.—Plan of Lamp Compartment

LAMP

A

INLETS FOR FRESH AIR

DOOR

Fig. 185

SLOPE

SLOPE

PERFORATED PLATE

CHIMNEY

2'3"

2'3"

Scale of feet and inches.

E OUTLETS

FLOOR

FLOOR

FLOOR

Fig. 184

H

J

Figs. 184 and 185.—Front Elevation and Horizontal Section of Rearer

B in Fig. 180, to hold the lamp, which can have a rectangular oil-container and be of the best and safest quality the pocket can afford. The floor is carried on small fillets, as at C (Fig. 180), and in the centre is cut a circle of about $5\frac{1}{2}$ ins. diameter to suit a heat-guard, as in Fig. 182, of sheet tin, zinc, or mica, to prevent the birds touching the hot chimney. On the underside of the hole in the floor is fixed an octagonal metal plate as in Fig. 183, pierced for the lamp-chimney and with a series of smaller holes all round, as shown.

Over the whole is arranged a removable zinc, tin, or sheet-iron radiator, as at D in Fig. 180, shown also in Fig. 179, where the top has been taken off this compartment. It is a great improvement on the usual flat commercial type, as by reason of its slightly pyramidal form it collects the gaseous air rising from the lamp and lets it gradually filter through the four outlet-holes in it (which might be of 1 in. diameter) into the upper space, whence is disperses through plenty of holes as at E (Figs. 180, 181, and 184). This helps to draw fresh air in from below, as does also the rising heat of the lamp-flame, which causes a gentle current of warmed fresh air to ascend through the holes in the metal plate (Fig. 183) and to distribute itself over the top of the heat-guard, as indicated by the arrows in Fig. 182, well above the chicks, which consequently feel no draught. The radiator is far easier to make than the complicated tanks and flues necessary for other systems, and could well be made by a novice. Made from one large sheet, it should be set out as in Fig. 186, bent and soldered up, and the edge turned over to avoid sharp angles. Alternatively it could be fashioned from two sheets, each cut as at F and G, and with the necessary laps for soldering. A strip might be attached to serve as a handle.

Sheet metal is also adopted for the corners of the sleeping compartment to prevent the chicks being squeezed into them. A rounded form is thus obtainable (as in Fig. 185), and gives a very neat and hygienic treatment. A sloping platform is required next the run, and can be hinged to form a door at night, and access (apart from that obtained by taking out the radiator) is given by the glazed door at H in Fig. 184, which is hinged on the front of the boarding, thus covering the edges of the opening all round. It is well above the chicks; but a glance through it will show whether the lamp is in order or not. The latter should be of the best type, and well tended, as a bad fit of smoking might prove fatal to the occupants. A chimney is necessary in order to carry the fumes right up to the radiator, and must be placed in position from above before the latter is put in. Inlets for air should be cut on the three exposed sides of the lamp compartment, as in Fig. 187 (but not in a direct line with the lamp), and a door (which need not be glazed in this case) arranged on the front as at J in Fig. 184.

The outside should be creosoted or painted, and the interior lime-whitened occasionally.

Rearer with Hot-Air Radiator.—This rearer (see Figs. 188 to 191) is not treated in so much detail as the preceding ones, as it only differs from them in the matter of heating, and the system employed can be adapted to various other types of appliance. Only the lamp- and sleeping-compartments are here shown. The first is about 8 ins. high, but should be adjusted according to the fittings employed, and the sleeping compartment is 12 ins. high, having sheet-metal corners as before, these being more easily warmed and less absorbent of moisture from the air than wood. In the centre of the floor is a circular hole fitted with a perforated plate and heat-guard exactly as described. Through this plate passes a chimney, as at A in Fig. 188, which can either be fitted into a gallery on the lamp-burner in the ordinary manner, or alternatively fixed with wires quite independently of the lamp, and finished with a funnel-shaped lower end, as shown, to gather the heat from the burner, which would then be one of the chimneyless type. If of metal, the chimney can have a piece of mica inserted to give a little light in the sleeping compartment at night.

On to the top of the chimney is fitted, by means of a socket, an air-tank or radiator of the type shown by Fig. 191, about 1 ft. 8 ins. in diameter and $2\frac{1}{4}$ ins. deep. This can be made specially to requirements, or a similar article can be obtained from makers of poultry appliances, together with the necessary flue, heat-guard, etc. The radiator is shown in section in Fig.

188, in which the currents of air set in motion by the lighted lamp are indicated by small arrows. Obviously the heat ascends the chimney, at the top of which it strikes a plate which distributes it over the entire

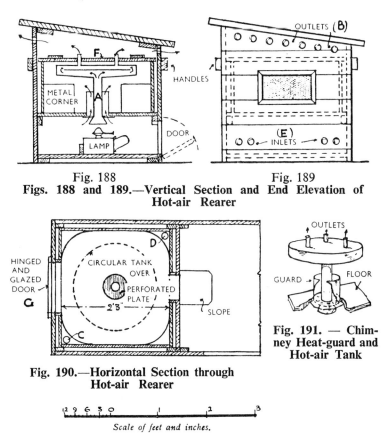

Fig. 188

Fig. 189

Figs. 188 and 189.—Vertical Section and End Elevation of Hot-air Rearer

Fig. 190.—Horizontal Section through Hot-air Rearer

Fig. 191. — Chimney Heat-guard and Hot-air Tank

Scale of feet and inches.

lower area of the circle, whence it gradually rises to the space between the upper surface of the plate and the top of the radiator, and thence through the three small outlets (see Fig. 191) to the space under the roof of the rearer. From this it finally disperses through rows of holes in the wooden sides as at B in Fig. 189. By this means a considerable surface of metal is gradually heated sufficiently to maintain any desired temperature, while none of the products of combustion can possibly reach the chicks.

Incidentally the heated chimney draws in fresh air from the lamp compartment through the perforated plate in the floor, warms it a little, and distributes it over the top of the heat-guard. Fresh air is so important a consideration that this ventilation might be supplemented by a couple of air inlets behind the metal corners, as at C and D in Fig. 190, and a plentiful supply of air to the lower compartment must be ensured by holes as at E in Fig. 189, placed near the corners only, so as to screen the lamp from draught.

A few outlets for exhausted hot air from the chicks will be required in the inner top boarding F (Fig. 188), and will facilitate the circulation from below. The air-tank can be supported on a couple of stout wires across the rearer under it, or by a wire extension of the heat-guard.

Access to the interior without moving the tank is provided by a glazed hinged door at the end (or front if more convenient), as shown at G in Fig. 190, and another door will be necessary for the lamp.

Other Rearers.—A rearer, suitable for any of the types having the lamp below the sleeping chamber, is shown in Fig. 192. The top inclines from one end to

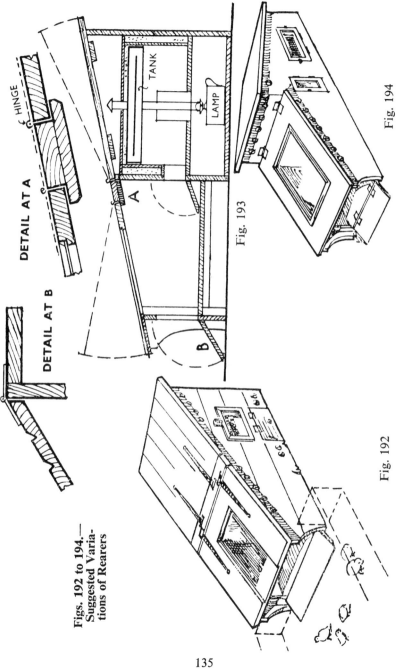

DETAIL AT A

HINGE

DETAIL AT B

TANK

LAMP

A

B

Fig. 193

Fig. 194

Fig. 192

Figs. 192 to 194.—
Suggested Varia-
tions of Rearers

135

the other, thus giving the most height just where it is required, as shown in the section in Fig. 193. Either a hot-air tank or a system of direct heating from the lamp can be adopted, although the former

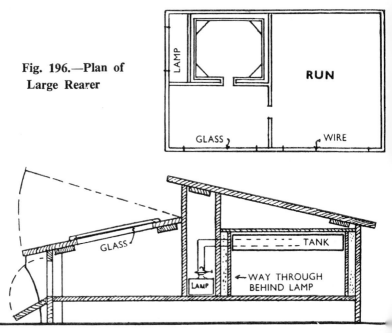

Fig. 196.—Plan of Large Rearer

RUN

LAMP

GLASS

WIRE

GLASS

TANK

← WAY THROUGH BEHIND LAMP

LAMP

Fig. 195.—Longitudinal Section through Rearer (see also Fig. 194)

only is indicated in Fig. 193. Here is shown a lamp compartment with a flue connected to a tank 9 ins. above the floor of a sleeping compartment, with saw-dust insulation, etc., as before, both spaces having doors and ventilation holes. The chicks' exit from the heated chamber consists of a small outlet fitted with a hinged slope, this forming a door at night, and the same principle applying to the slope at B, which, however, extends right across the end (see Fig. 192). Both should be splayed and grooved slightly, as in the detail of the part B.

For the top a stout rail as at A (Fig. 193) should be fixed across, and either rebated along both edges or composed of two thicknesses of wood as shown. Both portions of the slope are hinged to this by means of strap or " cross-garnet " hinges as shown, the upper part being composed of tongued boarding on ledges, and the lower, for preference, framed like a skylight or garden frame, in order to accommodate a small pane of glass which may be puttied in position. In use the glazed top can be raised slightly on occasion or turned right back, in which latter case an inner guard of wire mesh will be necessary.

Another type of rearer, best suited to cases in which the lamp is situated between the two usual compartments, is shown by Figs. 194 and 195. Internally it is quite on the usual lines. For the higher roof, plain boarding on ledges will suffice, but glass is desirable in the lower roof.

With this class of water-tank rearer the plan is almost always similar to that of Fig. 175, with the lamp accessible from one end only of its compartment. While this is the best arrangement for ordinary cases, it might well be modified, in the event of a very large appliance being required, to the form shown in Fig. 196. This gives exceptional access to the lamp.

CHAPTER XI

Follow-on Outdoor Chick-Rearers

IN unheated outdoor brooders the chicks generate their own heat rather than relying on artificial sources, and in the warmer months of the year such appliances prove a success.

The unheated outdoor rearer develops the chicks quickly, at the same time making them hardy and active. The young chicks may spend the full term of three or four weeks in a heated rearer, and then be transferred to an unheated follow-on brooder as an intermediate stage prior to removal to the poultry-house. Purchased growing chicks can be accommodated in it if desired.

The accommodation should be sufficient to avoid overcrowding and to ensure fresh air; but if made too large it is not likely to attain a sufficiently warm temperature. A unit from 2 ft. to 2 ft. 6 ins. square as the sleeping compartment is satisfactory. The run may be narrow, but should in all cases be at least 6 ft. in length.

Combined Nursery and Run for Fifty Chicks.— While in certain cases it may be a convenience to arrange a detachable run (as in the case illustrated in

Fig. 169), it is usually practicable to construct both nursery and run in a continuous range such as that illustrated in Figs. 197 to 204. This should usually be

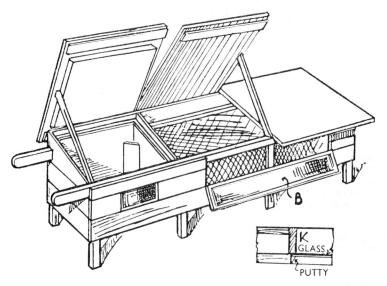

Fig. 197.—Unheated Rearer.   Fig. 198.—Detail of Glazing.

fitted with handles to facilitate rapid moving. Alternatively the larger types of appliance might conveniently be mounted on small wheels.

It is essential to guard against the risk of damp, which can be best avoided by mounting on legs or ledges; another risk is that of draughts. To prevent these, all but the front should be carefully enclosed, and the whole made close-fitting and composed of tongued-and-grooved boarding of 6 ins. (as in the present instance) or other convenient widths. When used with the edges horizontal, care should be taken to ensure that the grooved edge of a piece of match-boarding is undermost; if at the top it might possibly collect a certain amount of moisture.

Fig. 197 shows the brooder to consist of a nursery and run, the former enclosed by double walls of boarding to prevent the internal temperature being too quickly affected by outside conditions. The corners are cut off by means of angle-pieces 6 ins. wide as in Fig. 201, to prevent any chicks from being crushed into them. This compartment is lit by a small pane of glass in the front, and the whole is covered in by means of a sloping roof of boarding held together with ledges (see Fig. 203) and covered with good quality roofing felt. 'This makes the most serviceable but at the same time a very simple form of covering, as it can be made to hinge upwards or to lift right off as preferred. While the felt serves to some extent as an insulation, it will be all the better to arrange it with a double thickness of boarding as at A in Fig. 204. The spaces between the two thick-nesses, both of the top and sides, had best be packed very thickly with sawdust. For the bottom, which will, of course, be covered with peat moss or similar litter, the double thickness is unnecessary.

From the nursery an opening gives access to the run. At night this can be closed by means of a sliding door, as shown in Fig. 171, for the heated rearer, and it should be protected by means of a

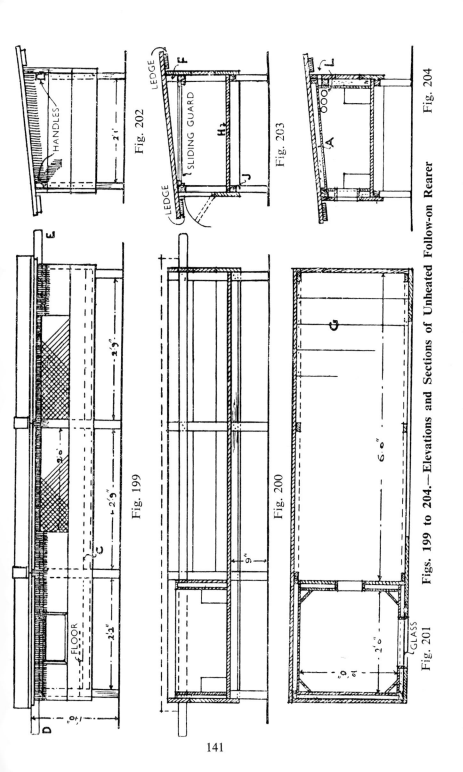

Fig. 202

LEDGE

F

SLIDING GUARD

LEDGE

H

J

Fig. 203

L

A

Fig. 204

HANDLES

2'1"

Figs. 199 to 204.—Elevations and Sections of Unheated Follow-on Rearer

E

2'5"

2'0"

4'2'5"

C

2'2"

FLOOR

D

1'0"

Fig. 199

9"

Fig. 200

G

6'0"

2'6"

2'0"

GLASS

Fig. 201

141

thick piece of baize, cut into strips fitting closely together when suspended, but allowing easy passage to the birds.

The run itself has boarded sides and floor, with two small apertures filled in with wire mesh at the front. These can also have a hinged glazed frame as at B in Fig. 197, capable of being closed in bad weather. The run is roofed in by means of two more sections of ledged and felted boardings, the central one of the three having painted fillets fixed along its edges, so that when it is put down last they will cover the joints between the sections. If hinged to open, these parts can be provided with struts, as in Fig. 197, thereby allowing bright sunshine free access to the interior, and keeping it aired and healthy. If left open in this way, wire guards are essential for the protection of the chicks. These might be provided for the run by means of a light frame, filled in with wire mesh and sliding on small fillets, as in Fig. 203. This can be moved along to whichever part of the run is intended to be left open at the time.

For the construction of the brooder, two sets of framework composed of deal about $2\frac{1}{2}$ ins. by $1\frac{1}{4}$ ins. will be required, the first consisting of four uprights 1 ft. 10 ins. high, a rail as at C, and a top rail projecting and rounded to form the handles as at D and E, the whole being halved together to the dimensions shown by Fig. 199. The other piece of framing is exactly similar, but with the uprights projecting above

the upper rail as at F in Fig. 203. Obviously these
two pieces of framing form the front and back of the
brooder. They are held together by the floor-boarding
G (Fig. 201) and H (Fig. 203), nailed on the tops of
the lower rails, and by the end-boarding shown in
Fig. 202. The back boarding is perfectly simple, and
that for the front is trimmed for the openings as in
Fig. 199. Note that the sides are taken well below
the floor all round (as at J in Fig. 203), in order to
keep off possible draughts from the latter. The partition between the two compartments can be readily
fitted, after which the inner casing of the nursery may
be put in hand, the window in this being contrived
with a lining as at K in Fig. 198, forming a small
rebate into which the glass can be puttied in the usual
way.

Ventilation must not be overlooked in the nursery.
Inlets should be provided by means of circular holes
bored in the bottom at the small triangular corners,
fresh air being thus introduced well above the chicks.
Outlets for warm vitiated air are essential, and should
be provided at the highest possible parts of the ends
and back, as indicated at L in Fig. 204. Where these
pass through the double boarding, it is a good plan to
drive a short length of $\frac{3}{4}$-in. or 1-in. pipe through
circular holes in the wood.

The details of the glazed screen to the front of the
run, sliding door, sloping roof, etc., call for no special
comment; but the entire work should be well painted

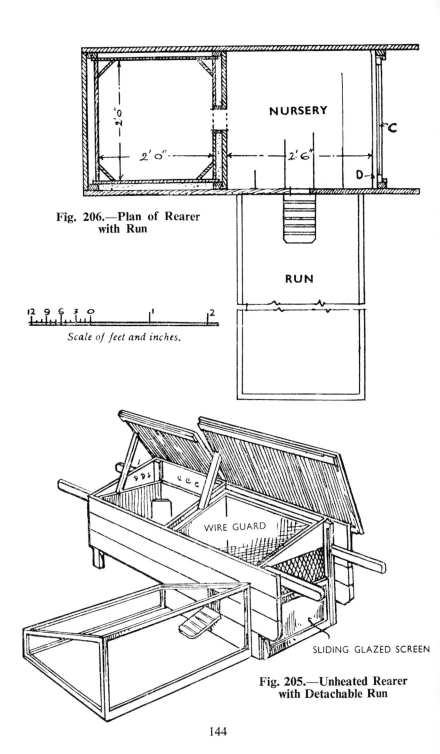

NURSERY

C

D

2' 0"

2' 0"

2' 6"

RUN

Fig. 206.—Plan of Rearer
with Run

12 9 6 3 0   1   2

Scale of feet and inches.

WIRE GUARD

SLIDING GLAZED SCREEN

Fig. 205.—Unheated Rearer
with Detachable Run

or stained in the usual way, the inside being periodically lime-whitened.

Unheated Brooder with Detachable Run.—This design (see Figs. 205 to 210) differs from the last described
in that it comprises a sleeping chamber very similar
to the nursery of the other but unlighted, a nursery in
place of the run, with light and ventilation from the
end, which is exceptionally sheltered by the projection
of the sides and roof shown in Fig. 205.   The door
shown gives access to a separate run constructed of
light framing and fine wire mesh, although it might
be as well to cover in some portion of the top with
boarding instead of wire.   It is necessary to move the
unit and run almost daily.

As before, this brooder consists first of all of two
sets of framing of about $2\frac{1}{2}$ ins. or 2 ins. by $1\frac{1}{4}$ ins.,
halved together as in Fig. 210, one set having the
three 6-in. top projections indicated by dotted lines,
and the other finishing flush along the line of the
handles.   In this case also they are held together
mainly by the boarded floor and ends, and covered
with boarded and felted roofs, either arranged to
hinge back, to lift right off, or slide along, while there
is also no difference in the double sides, corners and
door of the inner chamber.   Instead of the double
thickness of lid previously adopted, an alternative
arrangement is shown in Fig. 207.   Here there is a
small rebate, as at A, all round, taking an inner lid
in a horizontal position, and leaving an air-space

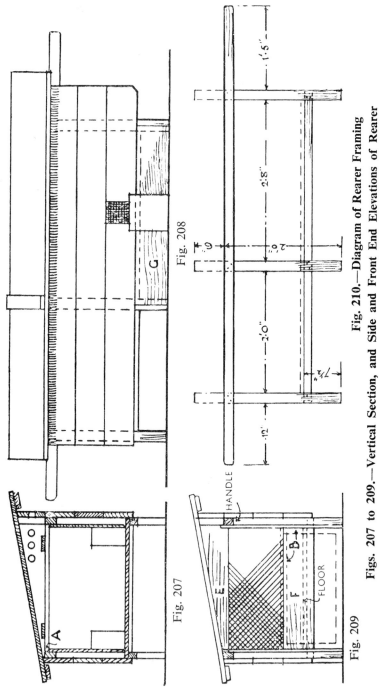

Fig. 208

Fig. 207

Fig. 209

HANDLE

FLOOR

Fig. 210.—Diagram of Rearer Framing

Figs. 207 to 209.—Vertical Section, and Side and Front End Elevations of Rearer

146

between this and the sloping roof. The inner lid consists of boarding on a couple of ledges shown in section, and it can be fitted with a wood or metal handle for removal. Ventilation is ensured by means of inlets behind the sloping corners as before, several holes bored in the centre of the inner lid as outlets, and further holes near the top of the back and side as shown in Fig. 205.

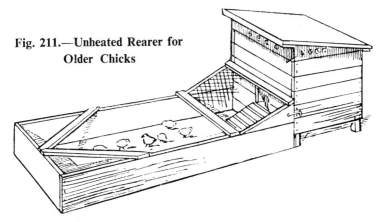

Fig. 211.—Unheated Rearer for Older Chicks

The nursery is exceptionally sheltered by means of the projecting boarding, while the open part of the end shown in Fig. 209 can be closed when considered advisable by means of a glazed sash, the position of which when fully open is as shown dotted at B. This sash is shown on plan at C in Fig. 206, where D represents the position of the top and bottom boards at E and F in Fig. 209, these being nailed to the inner faces of the end uprights, between which the sash should slide. It is of quite the ordinary type, and

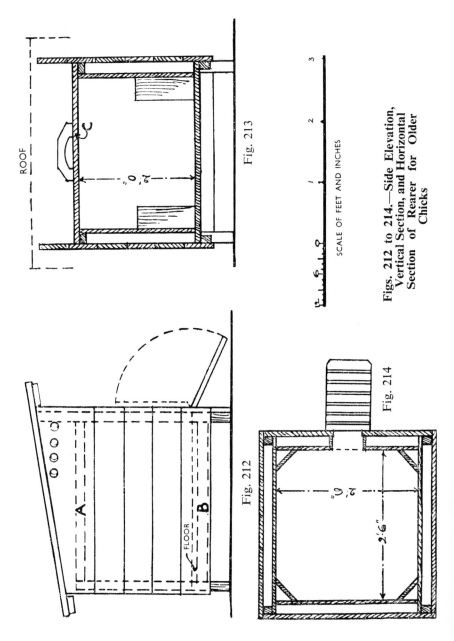

ROOF

Fig. 213

SCALE OF FEET AND INCHES

Figs. 212 to 214.—Side Elevation, Vertical Section, and Horizontal Section of Rearer for Older Chicks

Fig. 212

FLOOR

A

B

Fig. 214

148

should be kept in place with a couple of fillets fixed to the uprights. When raised it can be secured with a wood or metal pin fitting into a hole in the top board.

Next the run a central opening should be cut, and a board hinged on in such a way that when open it forms a slope down to the ground level, while when raised and fastened by a turnbuckle or simple catch, it securely fastens the entrance. A foothold should be given on the slope by either grooving this board at intervals, or fixing small strips of wood across it. In some cases it might be advisable to provide a door on each side of the nursery, so that the run could be placed where more convenient. Next the run the side boarding should be continued to the ground as at G in Fig. 208. A removable wire guard should be fitted on small fillets to protect the nursery when left open, as in Fig. 205.

Small Brooder for Older Chicks.—The very simple type of cold brooder shown by Figs. 211 to 214 is readily made, but offers less fully sheltered day-time accommodation, and for this reason is best suited to summer use and for chicks that have been kept in more protected surroundings until at least fledged. As these will have developed from their earlier stages, rather more space is allowed by making the nursery 2 ft. 6 ins. square. One cannot do better than raise this several inches clear of the ground, and make its roof in one slope removable for cleaning. The inner lining of the box might be dispensed with, provided that plenty of moss litter, etc., is provided; but it is a great safeguard against chills.

The framework comprises four uprights, framed up with two rails to either side, as at A and B in Fig. 212, the whole boxed up with grooved and tongued boarding about $\frac{3}{4}$-in. thick. As before, the top has an inner lid C (Fig. 213), fitted with ventilation holes and a wooden handle, the vent-holes in the sides being shown in Fig. 211, while fresh air would be admitted by means of the sloping corners (Fig. 214), which are still very necessary.

An inexpensive detachable run can be quickly made on the lines shown in Fig. 211, where the sides are merely boards covered in with wire at the top, and braced across with small battens as shown.

CHAPTER XII

Grain Distributor for Poultry

THE grain distributor described in this chapter is one of the best types put on the market. It is claimed that the fowls will quickly learn to feed themselves, thus saving labour on the part of the keeper, and the exercise of working the distributor will keep the birds healthy.

Fig. 215 gives a side view of the feeder. A is a circular hopper for holding the grain. This hopper is fitted with a coned lid B and a coned bottom, at the base of which is the grain-distributing valve C. Below the hopper is a coned deflector D, on which the grain falls and is thrown outward. The hopper, deflector, and lid, are made of fairly stout galvanized sheet-iron. The hopper is mounted on three iron legs E, which pass through the deflecting cone, and are from $\frac{3}{8}$-in. to $\frac{1}{2}$-in. in diameter, according to the size of the hopper. Below the deflector D is a bait cage F, which consists of a tube made of wire gauze or net about 8 ins. long by $1\frac{1}{4}$ ins. in diameter. The meshes should be just large enough to contain the grain without its falling through. The birds see and peck at this, thereby causing it to revolve, and as it is connected to a spindle G, when it turns it releases grain from the valve above. Either this bait tube should be capable of being raised or lowered on the spindle to

151

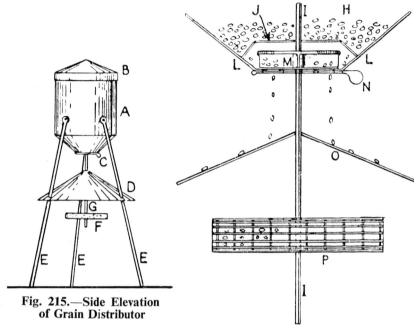

Fig. 215.—Side Elevation
of Grain Distributor

Fig. 216.—Details of Grain Valve

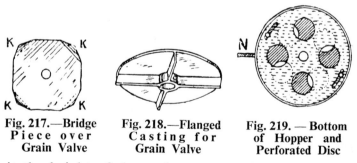

Fig. 217.—Bridge
Piece over
Grain Valve

Fig. 218.—Flanged
Casting for
Grain Valve

Fig. 219. — Bottom
of Hopper and
Perforated Disc

suit the height of the various types of poultry, or the
legs should be capable of adjustment.

Fig. 216 gives an enlarged view of the valve, and
on this the success or failure of the feeder depends.
H shows the bottom of the hopper, through which the

spindle of $\frac{5}{16}$-in. diameter steel I passes down to the bait cage. To prevent the full pressure of the grain bearing on the valve, a bridge piece J is provided. This consists of a piece of sheet-iron, first cut roughly to the shape of a four-pointed star, the points of which K (Fig. 217) are bent downwards, to bear on the cone of the hopper as shown at L (Fig. 216). A hole is drilled in the centre to a loose fit on the spindle, and the bridge can be made to a larger or smaller size, according to the capability of the grain to " flow." Below this is a circular casting about $1\frac{3}{4}$ ins. in diameter by $\frac{3}{8}$-in. total thickness M, secured to the spindle with a set-screw. This casting has four webs on the under-side as shown in Fig. 218, and as the spindle revolves these webs or fins pass the grain over the outlet holes. Four holes about $\frac{5}{8}$-in. in diameter are punched in the bottom of the hopper, a plan of which is shown by Fig. 219, and below this a disc with four holes to correspond is secured with two or three slotted rivets. A thumb-piece N (Figs. 216 and 219) is provided on this disc, and a reference to Fig. 219 will show that by rotating the bottom disc the size of the holes may be regulated to allow a smaller or greater quantity of grain to pass, or for larger or smaller kinds of grain. O (Fig. 216) shows the deflector cone, the use of which has already been described, and P the bait cage, which must be secured rigidly to the spindle by a set-screw or by some other means, and should be capable of being raised or lowered.

INDEX